HOOKED ON BOOKS

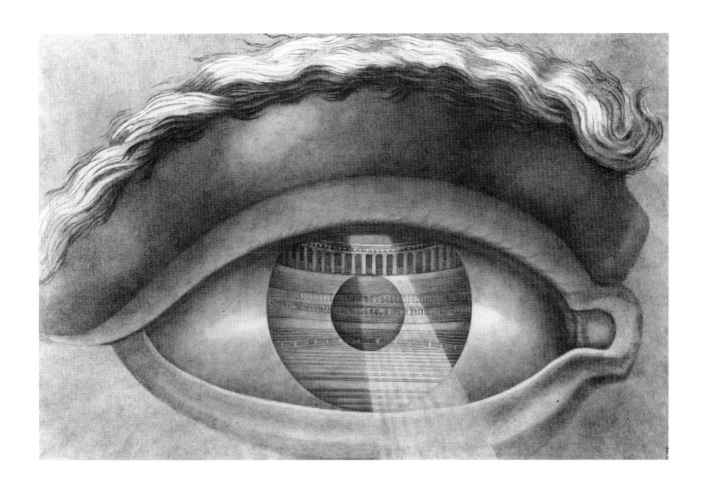

THE LIBRARY OF SIR JOHN SOANE
ARCHITECT
1753–1837

Curated by Eileen Harris and Nicholas Savage

SIR JOHN SOANE'S MUSEUM

Hooked on Books: The library of Sir John Soane, Architect 1753–1837
an exhibition at the Weston Gallery, Lakeside Arts Centre, University of Nottingham,
30 April – 30 August 2004, curated by Sir John Soane's Museum in collaboration with
Manuscripts and Special Collections, University of Nottingham

Supported by the
Resource/DCMS
Designation
Challenge Fund

Published in Great Britain 2004
by Sir John Soane's Museum
Reg. Charity No.313609

ISBN 0 9542284 6 4

Designed and typeset in Caslon and Albertina by Libanus Press, Marlborough
Printed by BAS Printers Limited, Salisbury

Front cover: Bookshelves in the Dining Room, 13 Lincoln's Inn Fields. Photo: Martin Charles
Back cover: Binding with the crest and crown of Napoleon and the arms and insignia of the King of Italy. See cat.9.3
Title page: The interior of the theatre at Besançon reflected in the pupil of an eye. See cat.1.1

CONTENTS

FOREWORD

Soane's intention in assembling his varied collections was to show 'the union and close connexion between Painting, Sculpture and Architecture – Music and Poetry'. His library, shelved in an ingenious array of bookcases on the ground floor of his house, played its part in this union, albeit unseen, as did the volumes of drawings which were often filed with the books. In his Study, for example, Soane described his books of value – his 'Macklin's Bible, Villalpandus, Le Musée François, and the Vitruvius Britannicus' side by side with a volume of original designs by Sir Christopher Wren. A litany of names conjured up all kinds of associations.

In spite of this the books in Soane's Library have never received the attention they really deserve: his paintings and antiquities are displayed in the Museum for all to see and since 1995 the drawings from his collections have been exhibited in the Soane Gallery. An exhibition of books, however, has always proved to be far more difficult in the confined spaces of the Museum. We are, therefore, particularly grateful to the Designation Challenge Fund for funding this exhibition – the first on Soane's books – and its tour, in conjunction with a project to re-catalogue the Library, as well as to Dr Dorothy Johnston and her team in the Department of Manuscripts and Special Collections at the University of Nottingham for their helpful collaboration in hosting the exhibition at the University's Weston Gallery.

Many thanks go to Dr Robin Middleton, Professor David Watkin and Paul Grinke for their advice and to Gillian Darley, Dr Alison Shell, Christopher Woodward, Simon Jervis, Helen Dorey and Stephen Massil for contributing to the introductory sections and catalogue entries. Margaret Schuelein, Jane Bush, Mick Mason and Stephanie Pickford worked on the conservation of the books and drawings, the book cradles and condition reports.

Finally, we are especially grateful to Susan Palmer who meticulously organised the exhibition, its tour to Nottingham and the production of the catalogue and to our two guest Curators, Dr Eileen Harris and Nick Savage who conceived the idea of the exhibition, selected the books and compiled the catalogue. We owe them so much for their years of dedication to the detailed catalogue of Soane's books which is underway and to their ceaseless promotion of a great architect's library.

Margaret Richardson
Curator, April 2004

CONTRIBUTORS TO THE CATALOGUE

The introductions to each section were written by : Gillian Darley (GD); Helen Dorey (HD); Eileen Harris (EH); Simon Jervis (SJ); Margaret Richardson (MR); Nicholas Savage (NS); Alison Shell (AS) and Christopher Woodward (CW).

Catalogue entries were compiled by : Eileen Harris; Stephen Massil; Susan Palmer and Nicholas Savage.

HOOKED ON BOOKS:
INTERPRETING SIR JOHN SOANE'S LIBRARY

We tend to think of the books we own as either useful or entertaining and of a 'library' as a place that is more or less conveniently arranged for us to find such books and to read them. Some people, it is true, are more interested in books as physical objects that seduce the eye or as means to decorate a room – designers of books and interiors have more in common than they realise. For nearly all of us an unloved and unread book earns a reprieve from the charity box on account of its being inscribed by a friend ('From Dolly for Xmas 1929'). For a few afflicted souls however, such as the Regency architect Sir John Soane (1753–1837), to part with even a tatty or unreadable book is to commit an obscure kind of sacrilege. For such unfortunates, every book is a potential vehicle for their memories and a possible touchstone for the renewal of themselves and others in the future.

The library that Soane assembled over the course of his long working life is most remarkable for three things: firstly, like his career, it was entirely of his own making; secondly, he appears (with very few exceptions) to have kept every book, pamphlet and scrap of printed paper even that came into his possession; and thirdly, most amazingly of all, this whole assemblage has survived intact – an extremely rare occurrence for any private library and quite unique in the case of an architect. Surely no better scenario could be imagined for interpreting someone's life and character through the books they owned. And yet, even in this optimum case, as we match the selection of books on display here with Soane's known interests and pursuits in life, art and literature – and, equally, puzzle over what seems unlikely and out of character – we would do well to remember that for him even the most practical book contained not merely what its author wrote (and could be found therefore in any *other* copy) but, much more importantly, what his imagination had added in reading it, using it and, most of all, possessing it.

Possession was for Soane always an act of the imagination. Books, through their permanency and defiance of time and capacity as vessels of memory, were potent triggers of feeling and association in his mind. Like many collectors before and since, Soane was particularly attracted by copies of books previously owned by famous people. His interest in what are known in the book trade as 'association' copies went deeper however than the harvesting of autographs and book plates that this type of collecting usually feeds on. What Soane prized above all was the way his possession of a book that had belonged to someone in the past whom he admired, could affirm his present judgement of both the book in question and its former owner. This is why, for instance, he bought Joshua Reynolds's copy of the 1791 edition William Chambers's *Treatise on civil architecture* even though he already possessed a copy that had been personally presented to him by the author. Such duplication somehow doubled the reflection of the importance of this seminal work in Soane's mind. Some of the multiple editions and duplicates in Soane's library are no doubt accidental acquisitions, due to imperfect cataloguing (he put his sons to this Sisyphean task with very limited success) and the exigencies of buying books in auctioneer's lots. Many however are by authors like Le Sage, Abbé Laugier or Fréart de Chambray whom we know he either loved to re-read or thought important to put into the hands of pupils in his office and students at the Royal Academy. Whether he really needed ten editions of Le Sage's *Gil Blas* to soothe his spirits or quite so many copies of Laugier's *Essay on architecture* to proffer to the young are questions that Mrs Soane may not have thought it her place to ask. It is more likely however that she knew her husband well enough to understand that, for him, to own ten copies of a book was to underline its value ten times.

For what we have in the great library that Soane left for all of us to profit by in his house in Lincoln's Inn Fields, is not a rational ordering of books as a source of knowledge but an incomparable demonstration of their power to stir the imagination. Provided it is given a reasonably sympathetic setting almost any library beyond a certain size can give a sense of the ceaseless industry and creativity of the human mind. The quite extraordinary setting of

De temps en temps j'aime à voir le vieux Père,
Et je me garde bien de lui rompre en visière.

FIG I 'Mephistopheles'. Lithograph by Eugène Delacroix. See cat.6.5

Soane's library however, in the finest and largest room of his house, is far from being merely sympathetic. For it was here that Soane entertained his guests at dinner, amidst a myriad of mirrors multiplying row upon row of gilt spines glinting in candle-light – another kind of duplication and emphatic underlining, but this time of the library itself rather than of a particular book within it. And it was here also, on 20 June 1835, that a special delegation of the 'Architects of England' marked the apotheosis of Soane as the founding father of the modern profession by presenting a gold medal to the octogenarian architect, who was so moved that he couldn't speak. Soane's placing of his library at the social centre of his house had nothing whatever to do with any practical use (dining rooms are far from ideal places to handle books) and everything to do with the fact that it was, I believe, the matrix from which he derived the entire arrangement of his home as a museum.

The taxonomic disorder that arises from the intricate display of disparate objects on every surface of every room and corridor in Soane's museum is precisely the same that occurs when books are placed randomly on a shelf. Accommodating such a constantly expanding library must have been an almost daily problem for Soane and even as an architect highly skilled in the manipulation of space, he needed all the ingenuity he could muster to make room for books in every possible nook and cranny he could find. When space is so tight the only way to arrange a library is by size, which of course militates against attempts to group books linearly by subject. So instead they began to flow like invisible lava, depositing fragments of his library in underground pockets throughout the house. Sometimes these deposits erupted in outcrops of glazed shelving, but more often they remained hidden behind cupboard doors. The reason for this is that, despite the showmanship of the Dining Room and the presence of many beautifully produced *éditions de luxe* in his collection, perhaps the least important aspect of a book for Soane was its physical appearance. And in a way that is strange to our modern eye, the same can be said about almost everything that he collected, since what mattered above all was the idea behind

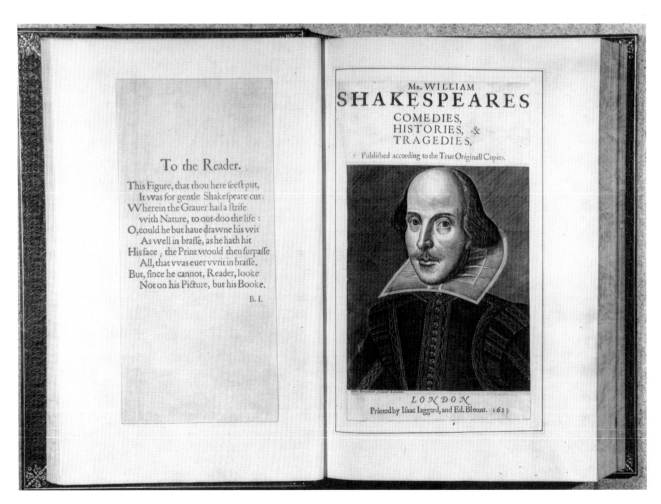

FIG.2 The celebrated 'First Folio' – a legendary rarity and Soane's greatest literary treasure. See cat.8.1

an object, the story that it told, and the connections and associations that it set off in the mind.

Soane was the younger son of a bricklayer and rose through immense hard work, good luck and a spark of ineluctable genius to become one of the greatest and most original architects England has ever produced. His life's work in the study, practice and teaching of architecture carried him on a dizzying journey that traversed every social strata in early 19th-century Britain, from the humblest hod-carrier, building labourer and artisan, through tradesmen and craftsmen, city merchants and bankers, politicians and bureaucrats, artists and writers, lawyers and doctors, and on up through all degrees of gentry, peers, diplomats, ministers of state and finally to the monarch himself. The collecting of books and making of a library repeatedly steadied Soane's private image of himself in this extraordinarily diverse world, in which his place and worth as a public figure were constantly open to scrutiny. As his friend Barbara Hofland observed, 'the aggregate wealth of the mighty minds that have preceded him' gave Soane the broad and safe 'foundation' he needed 'to raise the superstructure that may prove the temple of his fame'.

And yet... insofar as the 'temple of his fame' is not to be found in his rather dull lectures to the Academy students, and still less in the hopeless muddle he made of publishing his work in printed form, but rather in the daring originality of his achievement as an architect, then one quality above all others characterises his imagination, namely an impetuous, almost Byronic desire to risk transgression. Very unlike Byron however, there was also something distinctly Judaic in his character that drove him to seek atonement for his architectural 'transgressions' through the creation of a sanctuary for all those things – and in particular books – that had enabled him to reach the Promised Land of professional success and social status. When both his sons themselves transgressed, by spurning everything that he had gathered in this Ark, his fury and bitterness knew no bounds. Had either of them followed their father's wishes and applied themselves to architecture as he had done, there is little doubt that Soane's legacy would not have passed to the nation and his Museum as we know it today would not exist.

Soane's intense emotional investment in his house, library and museum in Lincoln's Inn Fields has left the

FIG.3 Engraved title-page designed by William Blake. See cat.7.3

imprint of his absence on everything that they contain. It is a kind of immortality, but not the living dynastic kind that he craved. For what he has left us is a mirror, in which we can never truly find him or his times, but only, much more strangely, ourselves and our own dreams.

This exhibition represents a tiny fraction of the 6,857 volumes contained in Sir John Soane's library. It is organised around ten themes or topics that were of great interest both to Soane and, in some cases, many of his friends and contemporaries. Subject to the considerable constraints of available space, the exhibition has been selected in the hope that it might encourage a much more detailed and considered exploration of these and other topics relating to Soane's library than has been possible on this occasion. A number of related prints, drawings and objects from Soane's collection have also been included in order to suggest the way in which his library and museum are interdependent.

NICHOLAS SAVAGE

FIG.4   The amphitheatre in the École de Chirugie in Paris. See cat.1.2

FIG.5   Views of Mount Vesuvius in the course of eruption, drawn by Pietro Fabris. See cat.5.1

Books on architecture are every bit as essential to an architect as a T-square and compasses. Thus, the French architect, E.-A. Petitot, portrayed himself in masquerade dress 'à la Grecque', leaning heavily upon a vast tome.

It was not only to educate himself in the fundamental principles of architecture and to pursue his personal interest in the subject that Soane collected books and pamphlets, drawings, models, fragments and casts. He also used all these things to inform and instruct the pupils in his office and the students at the Royal Academy, where he was Professor of Architecture from 1806 until his death.

Archaeological books concerned with the remains of Grecian and more especially Roman antiquities were of great interest to him, and were occasionally a source of inspiration. But, what he valued most were the published designs of the leading architects of his day, for it was primarily through such publications that he was able to keep up to date with the latest, most advanced and important achievements in the field. This is borne out by his purchases of Jacques Gondoin's *Description des Écoles de Chirurgie*, 1780, and C.-N. Ledoux's *L'Architecture*, 1804.

From the mid-18th century onwards, architects and critics were increasingly concerned with the experience of architecture – the emotions and feelings stirred by architectural forms and the spaces around them. Complex manipulation of perspective and theatrical design played a significant role in this new awareness. Its importance to Soane can best be seen in his own house at 13 Lincoln's Inn Fields, which is now the Soane Museum.   EH

1.1 Claude-Nicolas Ledoux (1736–1806)

L'architecture considérée sous le rapport de l'art, des moeurs et de la législation, Paris 1804. Plate 113: The interior of the theatre at Besançon reflected in the pupil of an eye. Unsigned etching. (Title-page)

This unusual plate, probably etched by the author himself, is an embodiment of Ledoux's concept of all architecture as a spectacle of which the architect is both author and spectator. Soane shared his interest in spatial compositions that stimulated the senses and the imagination of the viewer. He bought Ledoux's work as soon as it appeared in 1804, and was one of the first people in this country to do so.

1.2 Jacques Gondoin (1737–1818)

Description des Écoles de chirurgie, Paris 1780. Plate 29: Perspective view of the amphitheatre in the École de Chirurgie in Paris, showing an anatomical demonstration in progress. Engraving by C. R. G. Poulleau (1749–c.1790). (Fig.4)

Gondoin's surgical college, the École de Chirurgie, was the most celebrated building in Paris after the church of Ste.-Geneviève. After the amphitheatre was built and engraved, a Latin inscription was carved around the wall. A previous owner of this copy has added this in pencil, and also translated it as follows into French: 'Les Anciens Amphithéâtres Etoient Ouverts Pour Le Carnage des Homes – Les Notres Le Sont Pour Qu'Ils Apprenent A Vivre Longtems' [The ancient amphitheatres were open for the slaughter of men – ours are to teach them to live long]. Domes lit from above through a central opening were a recurring theme in Soane's work.

1.3 Ennemond-Alexandre Petitot (1727–1801)

Mascarade à la grecque d'après les dessins originaux tirés du cabinet de Monsieur le Marquis de Felino premier ministre de S.A.R., Parma 1771. Plate 10, a self-portrait of the architect E.-A. Petitot in Grecian masquerade costume, engraved by Benigno Bossi (1727–1792). (Fig.6)

A parody on the fashionable *goût grèc* which dominated all aspects of French design in the second half of the 18th century. The stuccoist, Benigno Bossi, collaborated with Petitot on the decoration of numerous Neapolitan interiors.

1.4 Ferdinando Galli Bibiena (1657–1743)

Dirizioni della prospettiva, teorica corrispondenti a quelle dell'architettura istruzione a' giovani studenti di pittura, e architettura nell' Accademia Clementina dell' Instituto delle Scienze, Bologna 1732. Plate 49: A stage set design showing an angular view of a monumental hall or gallery. Engraving.

Ferdinando Galli Bibiena was the most important member of the great Italian architectural family known for their theatre designs and decorations in the Baroque style. He is credited with the introduction in about 1690 of the corner stage set design or *scena per angolo* which gave a very much greater impression of space in a small set than the traditional central perspective. This small, affordable book of *Dirizioni* or instructions is a sequel to his earlier folio treatise, *L'Architettura civile*, 1711. It is addressed to the students of the Accademia Clementina in the Instituto delle Scienze in Bologna.

1.5 Abraham Bosse (1602–1676)

Moyen universel de pratiquer la perspective sur les tableaux, ou surfaces irreguliers, Paris 1653. Plate 31: A device for drawing a plain sphere or irregular three-dimensional object. Plate 32: Method for representing objects correctly on curved surfaces.

The first plate depicts a frame with several parallel lines stretched across it horizontally and one vertical line in the centre, which is used for plotting the representation of a sphere or an irregular three-dimensional object – such as a sculpted head – in perspective. The second plate concerning the optical distortion necessary for images painted on vaulted ceilings was added to copies of Bosse's book sold in or after June 1669. Abraham Bosse was one of the most skilful and prolific French engravers of the 17th century. His writings on perspective grew out of his friendship with the mathematician Gérard Desargues

(1593–1662) whose pioneering discoveries in this field were described and illustrated by him in an accessible form for the practical use of artists. Bosse taught perspective at the Royal Academy of Painting and Sculpture in Paris from the time of its foundation in 1648 until the loss of his post in 1665.

1.6a–b Drawing instruments belonging to John Soane

Pair of proportional dividers, *c.*1780.
Brass with metal tips SM X1207

Small tapered pocket instrument case, *c.*1800. Inscribed on top JS.

Wood covered with green shagreen (shark-skin), brass and silver mounts SM X296

L'Auteur des Figures à la Grecque

FIG.6 A self-portrait of the architect E.-A. Petitot in Grecian masquerade costume.

2 — THE ORIGIN OF ARCHITECTURE

A return to the simple origin of architecture came to be regarded in the second half of the 18th century as an effective means of stripping away the chaos of arbitrary rules founded on conflicting authorities, and establishing true principles based on reason in its place. This line of Enlightenment thought was of immense interest to Soane, especially when writing his Royal Academy lectures.

Vitruvius, a Roman architect and author active from 46 to 36 BC, was the first to trace the origin of classical architecture to the timber construction of the rustic cabins of primitive man. His *De architettura* is the only complete treatise on the subject surviving from antiquity. There are 14 copies in Soane's library, representing 12 different editions in Latin, Italian, French and English, dating from 1546 to 1826.

However, Soane's real guru, the driving force behind his unremitting pursuit of first principles, was the Abbé Marc-Antoine Laugier (1713–1769), a Jesuit priest and outstanding neo-classical theorist. Laugier's *Essai sur l'architecture*, 1753 – of which Soane owned no less than ten copies – identified the essential elements of the hypothetical primitive hut – free-standing columns resting on the ground, an entablature denoting a flat ceiling, and a sloping roof or pediment – as the only true sources of beauty in architecture. Everything for which no solid reason could be given was to be rejected. From these rigorous principles the path to modern minimalist architecture may be said to proceed. Accompanying the ideal primitive hut was the noble savage, whose natural goodness and simple virtues uncorrupted by society was the beau-ideal of Jean-Jacques Rousseau (1712–1778), another of Soane's heroes.

EH

2.1 Marcus Vitruvius Pollo (active 46 to 36 BC)

Les dix livres d'architecture … corrigez et traduis nouvellement en François … seconde edition … par M. Perrault, Paris 1684, Book 2, p. 35: Reconstructions by Claude Perrault (1613–1688) of the Colchian log cabin (fig.I) and conical Phrygian hut (fig.II). Illustration engraved by Jacques Grignon (c.1640 – after 1698). (Fig.7)

The left-hand figure is a reconstruction based on Vitruvius's description of a towering primitive log cabin of the kind built by the 'Colchi' or Crimeans in the forests of southern Russia. The right-hand figure shows another form of primitive construction consisting of a hollowed-out mound dwelling with a conical roof covered with turf, as built by the Phrygians on the barren plains of Turkey. The Colchian cabin shown here is a more accurate reconstruction than the one Perrault had published in the first edition of his translation of Vitruvius in 1673. Perrault was architect of the east front of the Louvre and the author of one of the most revolutionary and influential treatises on the five orders, *Ordonnance des cinq espèces de columns selon la methode des anciens*, Paris 1683.

2.2 Joseph François Lafitau (1681–1746)

Moeurs des sauvages ameriquains, comparées aux moeurs des premiers temps, Paris 1724. Plate 16. Unsigned engraving. (Fig.8)

A tribe of Canadian Iroquois Indians initiating a soothsayer. Lafitau was a Jesuit missionary who was sent to Canada in 1711 to study the customs of the Iroquois.

2.3 Marc-Antoine Laugier (1713–1769)

Essai sur l'architecture. Nouvelle edition, Paris 1755. Frontispiece designed and engraved by Charles Eisen (1720–1778).

The seated figure of Architecture turns her back on the broken remains of the classical orders and points instead to the original primitive hut constructed of living trees. The first edition of Laugier's *Essai*, published anonymously in 1753, had no plates at all. It was in response to criticism of his theories about the natural model of architecture that he introduced this frontispiece in the new, revised edition of 1755.

2.4 Marc-Antoine Laugier (1713–1769)

Essay on architecture, in which its true principles are explained and invariable rules proposed, London 1755. Frontispiece engraved by Benjamin Cole (*fl.*1730–55) after Samuel Wale (1721–1786).

A 'primitive hut' in the course of construction. This frontispiece to the English translation of Laugier's *Essay on architecture* is a misinterpretation of Laugier's concept of the origins of architecture. Like earlier Vitruvian illustrations, upon which it is based (see cat.2.1), it shows a first stage in the history of architecture rather than the allegory of first principles or fundamentals intended by Laugier and indicated in Eisen's engraving.

2.5 Joseph Michael Gandy (1771–1843)

'Architecture; Its Natural Model' 1838. Pen and ink and watercolour. SM XP12

The various geological formations, animal constructions (like the domed ant hills in the middle-ground), trees and plants from different climes brought together in this fantastic landscape offer a succession of natural models for man's artificial creations.

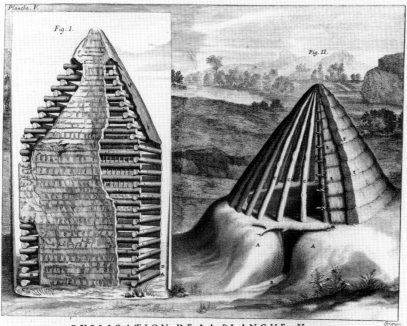

LIVRE II. 33

EXPLICATION DE LA PLANCHE V.

Cette Planche contient la maniere simple & grossiere dont les Anciens se servoient pour bastir leurs maisons avant que l'Architecture eust trouvé les moyens d'orner les Edifices & de les rendre commodes. La premiere Figure est pour les Cabanes de Cholcos. A B C les Arbres couchez de leur long sur terre à droit & à gauche. D E F les autres Arbres posez en travers sur les extremitez des premiers & qui enferment tout l'espace destiné pour l'habitation. Les autres Arbres qui sont mis en suite de la mesme maniere composent toute la hauteur des Murs. G G les Arbres accourcis vers les coins & retirez insensiblement & par degrez pour faire le toict en pyramide. H H les échalas mis entre les Arbres pour remplir leurs intervalles. I I la terre grasse soûtenuë par les échalas, dont on feint une grande partie avoir esté abbattuë, pour laisser voir la composition des Arbres appuyez par les bouts les uns sur les autres.

Dans la seconde Figure A A sont les petits tertres naturellement élevez, que les Phrygiens choisissoient pour les vuider, y creusant aussi des chemins B, pour entrer dans l'espace vuide. C C sont les perches qu'ils mettoient sur les bords du creux, & qu'ils lioient par le haut en pointe, sur lesquelles ils étendoient des cannes D D & du chaume E E avec des gazons F F pardessus.

qu'on employe en Architecture: Mais la verité est que c'é-
toit la coûtume de son temps à Rome où l'estude de la Philosophie estoit une chose rare & nouvelle, d'en faire para-
de avec une ostentation qui ne rendoit pas un auteur aussi
ridicule qu'elle seroit à present. Varron & Columelle en
une pareille occasion en usent de mesme que Vitruve; car
le premier au commencement de son livre d'Agriculture
qu'il dedie à sa femme, s'excuse sur son peu de loisir de

n'avoir pas traité la matiere de son ouvrage, comme il auroit
esté necessaire; & il luy conseille pour suppléer à ce défaut de
lire les livres des Philosophes, dont il luy en nomme jusqu'à
cinquante, & entr'autres Democrite, Xenophon, Aristote,
Theophraste, Architas & Magon, qui ont tous écrit ou en
Grec, ou en langue Punique. L'autre, sçavoit Columelle, dit
qu'il faut qu'un Jardinier & un Laboureur ne soient gueres
moins sçavans en Philosophie, que Democrite & Pythagore,

I

FIG.7 Reconstructions by Claude Perrault of the Colchian log cabin (fig.I) and conical Phrygian hut (fig.II). See cat.2.1.

In the lower right-hand corner there is a primate prototype of the Vitruvian primitive hut, constructed and occupied by apes. The ape, however, is only interested in apeing the vegetable kingdom, and is completely oblivious to the columnar fragments and monumental rocky caverns around him. That awareness waited for civilised man.

Having studied the natural world, Gandy concluded that the origin of architecture was not to be found there, but rather in Noah's Ark, which is shown in the upper part of the picture emerging from the clouds atop Mount Ararat.

'Architecture; Its Natural Model' was the last of five works exhibited by Gandy at the Royal Academy from 1836 to 1838 as part of an unfinished megalomaniac scheme that was to consist of 1,000 drawings like this one forming a world history of architecture entitled 'Comparative Architecture'.

Although Soane died shortly before this particular work was shown, he certainly knew about it from Gandy's announcement in the Royal Academy exhibition catalogue of 1836. The painting remained in the Gandy family until 1946 when Henry Gandy, the artist's great grandson, presented it to the Soane Museum.

FIG. 8 The initiation of a soothsayer among the Iroquois Indians (detail). See cat. 2.2.

When Napoleon's armies invaded Egypt in 1798 they were accompanied by Dominique Vivant-Denon (1747–1825) and 167 'savants' (i.e. learned men), who recorded the culture and natural history of ancient and modern Egypt in publications that created a wave of 'Egyptomania' across Europe and gave birth to modern Egyptology.

Soane acquired two copies of Denon's *Voyage dans . . . Égypte pendant les campagnes du Général Bonaparte*, Paris 1802, and translated passages from it for his Royal Academy lectures in which he praised the awe-inspiring qualities of ancient Egyptian architecture. Finally, on 12 September 1835, two days after his 82nd birthday, Soane took delivery of a copy of the *pièce de resistance* of any collection of books on Egypt – the *Description de l'Égypte*, 1809–29 – a monumental 20-volume record of thirty years' French scholarship in the region.

Soane's interest in Egypt was also directly stimulated by a rather different figure – a circus strong-man turned archaeologist and explorer named Giovanni Battista Belzoni (1778–1823). In 1817 Belzoni had entered the tomb of the Egyptian pharaoh Sethi I in the Valley of the Kings and discovered a great marble sarcophagus lying in a 'hall of pillars'. When the sarcophagus arrived in London in 1821, an exhibition opened at the Egyptian Hall in Piccadilly featuring a one-sixth scale plaster model of the tomb, lit as if at the moment of Belzoni's discovery. Soane visited this exhibition on 8 June 1822, little realising that his finest hour as a collector would come two years later with the purchase of Belzoni's actual sarcophagus and the installation of this great relic of the sublime mysteries of Egypt as the centrepiece of his own Museum.   HD

3.1 Christian Hertzog (d.1728)

Essay de mumio-graphie, Gothe 1718.
Letterpress title-page

This is an early description of an Egyptian mummy, which the author, an apothecary and botanist, considered to be one of the rarest and most curious he had ever seen in Europe. His account is dedicated to Frederick II, Duke of Saxe Gotha, an early collector of Egyptian antiquities.

3.2 Luigi Mayer (*c*.1755–1803)

Views in Egypt, Palestine, and other parts of the Ottoman Empire, London 1804. Plate facing p.22: 'Head of the Colossal Sphinx'. Hand-coloured aquatint, drawn by Luigi Mayer, engraved by and under the direction of Thomas Milton (*c*.1743–1827).

The German artist Luigi Mayer travelled to Asia Minor and the Near East in 1792 with Sir Robert Ainslie, the British Ambassador to the Ottoman Empire. On his return to Europe the many drawings he had made were engraved and published in two volumes. The hand-coloured plates in this book vividly convey scenes of both contemporary life in Egypt and Palestine and the great monuments of ancient Egypt in which there was much interest in England at this date, fuelled by the Egyptian campaign of Napoleon. The colossal figure of the Sphinx at Giza, near Cairo, shown

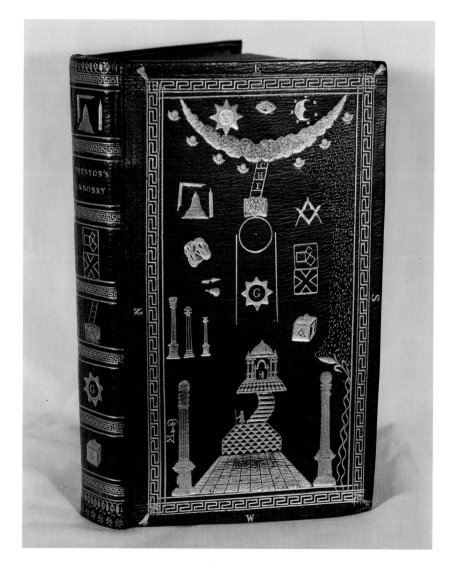

FIG.9 Book binding in dark blue calf tooled in gilt with Masonic symbols. See cat.3.3.

here as it was at the end of the eighteenth century when it was still almost completely covered with sand, made a huge impression on western travellers.

3.3 William Preston (1742–1818)

Illustrations of Masonry, 12th edition, London 1812. Binding: contemporary dark blue calf, tooled in gilt with Masonic symbols. (Fig.9)

Freemasonry looked to Egypt as the source of knowledge of building since the Israelites were supposed to have learnt the skills of building in stone from the Egyptians. There was a close connection between the story of the Israelites' captivity in Egypt, the use of the cubit as a unit of measurement, and the legends of the Craft and Solomon's Temple. At the beginning of the nineteenth century Egyptian influence on Freemasonry was particularly strong, especially on the Continent. For Soane, this book had a practical use, since he was, from December 1813, Grand Superintendent of Works, or Architect, to the United Grand Lodge of England. Practicality apart, Soane's involvement in Freemasonry ties in with his interest in architectural origins and wider sources of symbolism.

3.4 Alexandre Lenoir (1761–1839)

La Franche-maçonnerie rendu à sa véritable origine, Paris 1814. Plate facing page 244: 'Epreuves Par Les Quatre Élémens, Qui se Pratiquoient dans la Réception des initiés à Memphis'. [Trials by the four elements [earth, air, fire and water] used in the admission of initiates to Memphis]. Engraving by Louis Petit (1760–*c.*1812) after a drawing by Jean-Michel Moreau, *le jeune* (1741–1814).

Lenoir's text describes the initiation rites of the Freemasons and traces them back to their Egyptian origins. The literal illustration by Moreau *le jeune* shows a mysterious subterranean (earth) cavern, supported by Egyptian columns, in which an initiate flees from the fire on the right, swims the water, and ascends a hatch on the left to the air.

3.5 Egyptian Hall, Piccadilly (1819)

Catalogue of the Roman Gallery of Works of Art, and the London Museum of Natural History, London 1819. Printed front wrapper. (Fig.10)

The front wrapper of this sale catalogue bears a wood engraving of the striking façade of the Egyptian Hall in Piccadilly, designed and erected by the architect Peter Frederick Robinson (1776–1858) in 1811–12. Known officially as the London Museum, it was built as an exhibition building to house the collection of 'upwards of Fifteen Thousand Natural and Foreign Curiosities, Antiques, and Productions of the Fine Arts' belonging to the showman William Bullock. This catalogue covers the first six days of the sale in which the contents of Bullock's museum were dispersed in April and May 1819. The Hall itself was demolished in 1905.

3.6 Egyptian Hall, Piccadilly (1821)

Description of the Egyptian tomb discovered by G. Belzoni, London 1821. Letterpress title-page and engraved map showing the place on the west bank of the Nile where Belzoni discovered the tomb of Sethi I.

This pamphlet describes the tomb of the Egyptian pharoah Sethi I discovered by Giovanni Battista Belzoni in the Valley of the Kings on 17 October 1817. Belzoni recounted his discoveries in Egypt in his *Narrative of the operations and recent discoveries . . . in Egypt and Nubia*, London 1820, a copy of which Soane also owned. This shorter description was produced as a guide to the exhibition of his finds and a reconstruction of two of the chambers of Sethi's tomb with their vivid wall paintings, which opened at the Egyptian Hall in May 1821.

3.7 a–b Two faience ushabtis, xxvith dynasty

SM S148 and S149

Ushabtis were small models of people which the ancient Egyptians placed in tombs, both to represent the deceased and to do all the necessary work in the after-life. These two were given to Soane in 1831 by his friend the artist Maria Cosway (1760–1838), who in turn had been given them by Denon, who had picked them up in Egypt.

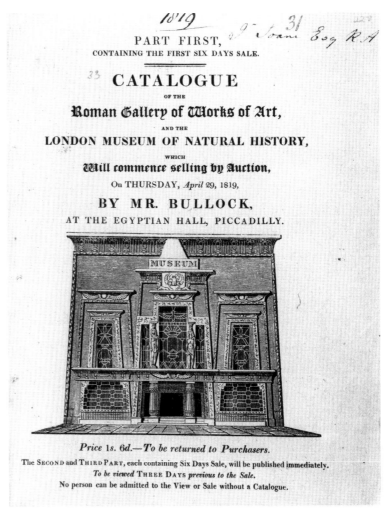

FIG. 10 Egyptian Hall, Piccadilly (1819). Printed front wrapper of sale catalogue. See cat.3.5.

Soane was a classicist. Greece and Rome were his inspirations. The architects he admired used a classical language, and when his revered master, George Dance, deviated into Indian at the London Guildhall, Soane's reaction was sour. And yet . . . Soane collected Indian miniatures, Chinese porcelain and Gothic fragments. His greatest treasure, the alabaster sarcophagus of Sethi I, was Egyptian. When he celebrated its purchase at a candle-lit party in 1825 it glowed in the shadows, evoking the world of Freemasonry and the Eleusinian mysteries, exotic, primitive and poetic.

In 1834 Soane purchased twelve Peruvian vases 'found in the tombs of the aboriginal Indians and supposed to have been used in their sacrifices'. He had earlier acquired Antonio del Rio's account of the discovery of a Mayan city, Palenque, and owned a prospectus for Lord Kingsborough's monumental *Antiquities of Mexico*. Doubtless Soane also visited William Bullock's Mexican exhibition, held in the Egyptian Hall in Piccadilly in 1834.

Perhaps Soane was attracted to Racknitz's great work on taste in interior decoration and architecture by its spectacular illustration of a Mexican interior. He certainly must have been deeply impressed by Racknitz since he acquired two copies of this very rare and expensive book, one in a luxury binding that cost him six and a half guineas in 1826.

Soane did not read German. For him the principal appeal of Racknitz's work must have been its beautiful plates, which presented an architectural universe in parallel, Tahiti side-by-side with French rococo, Gothic contrasted with 1760s neo-classicism – a universal vision embracing both primitive roots and modern sophistication. SJ

FIG. 11 A room fitted out in the Mexican taste. See cat. 4.1a

4.1a-e Joseph Friedrich Freiherr zu Racknitz (1744–1818)

Darstellung und Geschichte des Geschmacks der vorzüglichsten Völker [i.e. 'Description and History of the Taste of the Leading Nations'], 3 volumes, Leipzig 1796–98. Hand coloured etched plates designed by Christian Friedrich Schuricht (1753–1832)

(a) A room fitted out in the Mexican taste; in the background the great temple in Mexico. (Fig.11)

(b) A Tahitian building; in the background a procession led by the King of Tahiti greets a group of English soldiers with a sign of peace.

(c) Specimens of patterns with which Tahitians decorate their textiles.

(d) Interior of a house in Siberia.

(e) A Russian sleigh.

In 1768 Racknitz, the son of a courtier, himself became a courtier at the Electoral Court of Saxony in Dresden. In 1790 he was given charge of the theatre and the chapel, and in 1806 of the kitchens. A polymath, he published his own musical compositions, and books or articles on the history of art, on botany, and on geology. He also formed notable collections of natural history, minerals, botanical specimens, insects and shells. He was a patron of modern artists and had close relationships with the two leading architects active in Saxony during his lifetime, Christian Traugott Weinlig (1739–1799) and Christian Friedrich Schuricht (1753–1832). It was Schuricht who designed the spectacular illustrations for Racknitz's *Darstellung und Geschichte*.

Racknitz used a wide variety of sources in his research for this book. Examples include the 1777 Leipzig edition of William Robertson's *The History of America* and the Dresden Codex, in the Royal Library, for Mexico; Frederik Ludvig Norden's *Voyage d'Egypte et de Nubie*, Copenhagen 1755, for Egypt; William Chambers's *Designs of Chinese Buildings, Furniture, Dresses, Machines and Utensils*, London 1757, for China; De Lesseps's *Journal historique* of the Comte de La Pérouse's voyage, Paris 1790, for Kamchatka; Wendel Dietterlin's *Architectura*, Nuremberg 1598, for the old German taste; the Leipzig 1786 edition of Robert Orme's *Historical Fragments of the Mogul Empire*, London 1782 [–1783], and the Hamburg 1793 edition of William Hodges's *Travels in India*, London 1793, for India; and James Murphy's *Batalha*, London 1795, and Horace Walpole's *Description of the Villa . . . at Strawberry Hill*, London 1774 [–1784], for Gothic.

In all, the 'Description and History' covers twenty-four styles – modern, historic and exotic – in as many chapters, each illustrated by two colour plates, and two carefully tailored engraved ornaments. It is a monument to the systematic pursuit of information, which was such a feature of the German Enlightenment. Soane must have found the sheer range of Racknitz's examples fascinating, from Mexico to Siberia, and probably admired his illustrations for their combination of beauty and learning.

4.2 Edward King, Viscount Kingsborough (1795–1837)

Antiquities of Mexico, London [c.1830]. Letterpress leaflet. Prospectus for subscribers.

Edward King, Viscount Kingsborough, was converted to the study of Mexican antiquities by the sight of a Mayan manuscript in the Bodleian Library in Oxford, where he studied from 1814 to 1818. His ambitious publication on the *Antiquities of Mexico*, published in nine volumes from 1830 to 1848 and never completed, bankrupted him, and he died imprisoned for debt in Dublin in 1837. His researches led him to believe that Mexico had been colonised by the Israelites. 'Augustine Aglio', who appears to have issued this prospectus as Kingsborough's agent, is better known as Agostino Aglio (1777–1857), a landscape painter from Cremona, who became friendly with the architect William Wilkins (1778–1839) in Rome, and settled in England in 1803. Soane was not sufficiently tempted by this prospectus to become a subscriber and never acquired a copy of Kingsborough's book for his library.

4.3a Ancient Peruvian vessel
with handle-shaped spout and painted geometric decoration.

Baked clay, painted SM MP154

4.3b Ancient Peruvian vessel
in the form of an animal, seated on a square base with a ring handle, carrying a human head.

Baked clay SM MP162

Two of the group of twelve Peruvian pots purchased by Soane in 1834. Soane remarked of them: 'I doubt their antiquity – but they are uncommon'.

On 5th January 1779 Soane made his first visit to Pompeii and as the guards had strict orders to prevent visitors from making drawings of the ruins, made his sketches 'by stealth and by moonlight'. Later in the month he scaled Vesuvius, the volcano which had buried the twin cities of Herculaneum and Pompeii on the 24th and 25th of August 79 AD. He later made a second visit to Pompeii, making many more drawings on-the-spot, and was fascinated by the immediacy of ancient Roman life that was being revealed at the time – the evidence of unknown building types, ornamental motifs and Pompeian decoration that were to play such a major role in the development of European taste.

In the same spirit of rational exploration Sir William Hamilton, who was British Ambassador in Naples from 1764, examined at first hand Vesuvius and the 'campi flegrei' – literally 'burning plains' – of the volcanic area around Pozzuoli to the west of Naples. With that characteristic trait of Enlightenment enquiry, he had little time for anything he could not directly observe himself. His magnificent publication on the subject was based on letters he had sent to the Royal Society in London and was intended to insure, by the beauty and accuracy of its depiction of volcanic activity and geology, that henceforth 'this tremendous operation of nature will now be consider'd in a CREATIVE rather than a DESTRUCTIVE light'.   MR

5.1 Sir William Hamilton (1730–1803)

Supplement to the Campi Phlegræi being an account of the great eruption of Mount Vesuvius in the month of August 1779. Communicated to the Royal Society of London . . . , Naples 1779. Dedicatory frontispiece. Hand-coloured engraving after Pietro Fabris (1756–1779). (Fig.5)

The first volume of *Campi Phlegræi* – containing 54 gouache and watercolour etchings of the volcano and the surrounding area, made from 'drawings taken and colour'd on the spot' by Pietro Fabris under the strict supervision of William Hamilton – was published in 1776. Three years later a *Supplement* was published with five additional plates, including a dedicatory frontispiece with six views of Mount Vesuvius, one showing its 1760 eruption and the others the eruption in August 1779, the very year of Soane's visit. Soane purchased the complete work in a fine binding for £20 in 1799.

Pietro Fabris is credited with the introduction of the bodycolour (gouache) technique to Naples in the 1760s; his influence can also be seen in the work of the Welsh painter, Thomas Jones, to whom Hamilton lent a copy of *Campi Phlegræi* in 1782.

5.2 John Hayter (1756–1818)

A report upon the Herculaneum Manuscripts, London 1811. Letterpress title-page and hand-coloured etched frontispiece by S.J. Neele (1758–1824). (Fig.13)

This striking hand-coloured etching shows several flourishing clumps of papyrus, or paper reed, the aquatic plant that had furnished the raw materials for manuscripts. This is an important work in the history of manuscript conservation. Hayter describes the largely unsuccessful attempts to unroll the carbonized manuscripts found in the Villa of the Papyri at Herculaneum. Only recently have new methods been devised for opening further rolls with much improved results.

5.3 Charles-Nicolas Cochin (1715–1790) and Jérôme Charles Bellicard (1726–1786)

Observations sur les antiquités d'Herculaneum, 2nd edition, Paris 1755. Plate facing p.1. Unsigned engraving.

A section and view of the crater of Vesuvius, which Cochin had surveyed in 1749–50. Swarms of tourists are depicted on its slopes.

5.4 Pompeo Sarnelli (1649–1724)

La guida de forestieri curiosi di verdere, e di riconoscere le cose piu memorabili di Pozzuoli, Baja, Cuma, Miseno, Gaeta . . . , 4th edition, Naples 1768. Letterpress title-page and engraved frontispiece.

This popular guidebook to Naples and its region was first published in the late seventeenth century. The frontispiece depicts the site of the tomb of the Roman poet Virgil (70–19 BC) and what was then thought to be the entrance to the grotto of the Sybil at Pozzuoli. The grotto, which is now known to have been in fact at Cumae, was one of the most famous of all ancient sanctuaries, being where Aeneas, the hero of Virgil's poem the *Aeneid*, came to consult the Sibyl or prophetess. An inscription on the front free end-paper of this book shows that it once belonged to Maria Hadfield (1760–1838), later married to Richard Cosway. A life-long friend of Soane's, she had first met him in Italy during his Grand Tour, but it is not known whether it was at this or some later point that she gave him this book.

5.5a A fragment of painted stucco from Pompeii

SM L130

Soane picked up this fragment of painted stucco on one of his visits to Pompeii and brought it back to England with him. It may have inspired his choice of 'Pompeian red' for his Library and Dining Room at 13 Lincoln's Inn Fields.

FIG.12 The Grotto of the Sybil at Pozzuoli. See cat.5.4.

5.5b A fragment of painted stucco from Pompeii

SM L131

This more elaborate piece of moulding was picked up at Pompeii in 1818, and given to Soane as a present in July 1820 by Miss Swinnerton, the daughter of one of his clients, Thomas Swinnerton, for whom he built a farmhouse at Butterton in Staffordshire.

5.6 Attic stem-less cup

late 5th century BC.
Painted terracotta SM L34

This antique vase, with an incised pattern of honeysuckle on the inside, is one of a number in Soane's collection, displayed in profusion around his Dining Room and Library.

FIG. 13 Clumps of papyrus or paper reed. See cat.5.2.

More than for most of us perhaps, there were *demons* in Soane's life that demanded their due. Humour, fantasy, role-playing, and above all the creation of a unique house, museum and library for his *familiar* spirits to inhabit, helped to soothe *devils* of insecurity about his achievement as an architect, of private bitterness over the ingratitude of his sons, and of intense grief for the loss of his wife Eliza.

The key here, as for all collectors, is the special power that is conferred through possession, which comes precisely at the moment of full surrender to what one desires, and therefore utter possession by it. Soane's fantasies of absorption by his creation, of immurement as Padre Giovanni in his Monk's Cell, and of some future excavation of Lincoln's Inn Fields in which the ruins of his house and possessions would yield no clue to his true identity – he imagined that they might be mistaken for a *magician's lair* – had a logical outcome in his decision to leave his house and all its contents to the nation as a permanent memorial of his *absence*.

The immortality of Soane's genius – purchased in his lifetime through driving ambition, self-centredness and the sacrifice of familial comforts in a lonely old age – was a *Mephistophelian* bargain, the after-effects of which are still strong enough today to raise the hairs on the back of your neck, especially after dark in the many rooms in his house where mirrors seem to harbour *phantasms* of his form moving in silence through the shadows. NS

6.1 Anonymous

A true and faithful relation of the sad and dreadful accident which lately happen'd by Lincoln's Inn Fields, in the person of a maiden gentlewoman, whose body is possess'd by an evil spirit, London 1691. Letterpress title-page. (Fig.14)

We do not know when, why, or from whom Soane acquired this scrap of sensationalism, but at a fair guess he was probably struck like us by the coincidence of its association with the London square in which he lived.

6.2 Daniel Defoe (1661?–1731)

A system of magick; or, a history of the black art, London 1728. Engraved frontispiece by Gerard van der Gucht (1696–1777). (Fig.15)

This frontispiece depicts the traditional image of the necromancer or magician summoning spirits in his 'cell' or a private study, lined with the books and objects he needed to practice the 'black art'. The artist 'Eberlein' has not been traced.

6.3 Jean de La Fontaine (1621–1695)

Contes et nouvelles en vers, Amsterdam [i.e. Paris], 1762. 'Le Diable de Papefiguière'; vol. II, etched plate facing p. [149], designed by Charles Eisen (1720–1788). (Fig.16)

'The collector's book *par excellence*', this 1762 *édition-de-luxe* of La Fontaine's satirical tales of trickery and lust triumphing over naivety and innocence is one of the most famous

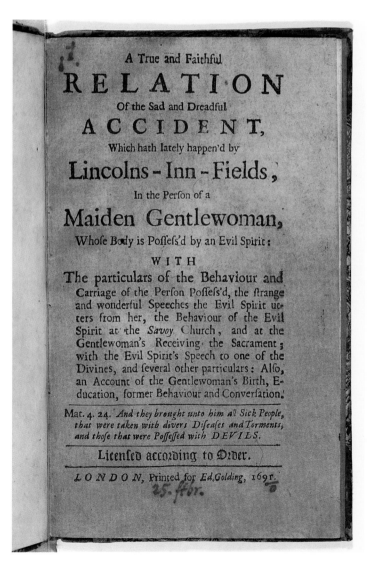

FIG.14 Title-page of an anonymous 17th-century account of possession by an evil spirit. See cat.6.1.

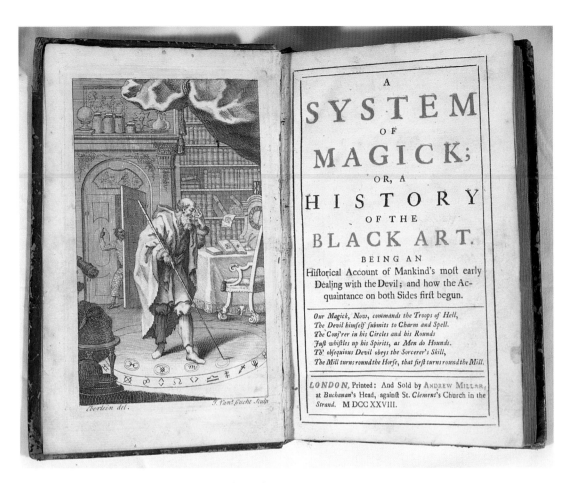

FIG.15 The necromancer summoning spirits from the dead. See cat.6.2.

illustrated books of the eighteenth century. Financed by the unlimited resources of the 'Fermiers Généraux' (i.e. tax collectors) of Paris and most exquisitely printed, it was illustrated by Charles Eisen (1720–1778) and Pierre Choffard (1730–1809), two of the greatest masters of *fête galante* book illustration of the period. Described by the Goncourt brothers as a product of 'one of the handsomest disbursements of witty and sensual money of Louis XV's reign', this is a book that almost any self-respecting bibliophile of Soane's day would have wanted to possess. Needless to say Soane's copy includes several of the more risqué (or 'découverte') versions of Eisen's plates that were particularly prized by collectors.

6.4 Samuel Taylor Coleridge (1772–1834) and Robert Southey (1774–1843)

The Devil's walk; a poem. By Professor Porson. Edited . . . by H.W. Montagu . . . Illustrated . . . after the designs of R[obert] Cruikshank, London [1830?]. Wood-engraved frontispiece and letterpress title-page. 'From his brimstone bed at break of day, / A walking the Devil's gone, / To visit his snug little farm the Earth, / And to see how his stock goes on.'

A mock scholarly edition of a *jeu d'esprit* disowned at birth by its true parents (i.e. Coleridge and Southey) and 'fathered' here instead (with tongue firmly in cheek) on the celebrated Greek scholar and Cambridge don Richard Porson (1759–1808).

6.5 Johann Wolfgang von Goethe (1743–1835)

Faust, tragédie de M. de Goethe, traduite en français . . . et ornée d'un portrait de l'auteur et de dix-sept dessins composés . . . et executés sur pierre par M. Eugène Delacroix, Paris 1828. Mephistopheles: 'De temps en temps j'aime à voir le vieux Père, / Et je me garde bien de lui rompre en visière' [I like to see the governor now and then and to take good care to keep relations civil.]. Lithographed plate at end of 'Prologue' (facing p.15). (Fig.1)

This famous image of Mephistopheles shows him in his true colours exulting after the Almighty has given him leave to tempt Faust. Eugène Delacroix (1798–1863) was inspired to illustrate Goethe's *Faust* after seeing a London production in 1825. A brilliant and embattled young painter, Delacroix set out to 'astonish the middle classes' with the force and freedom of his visual interpretation of Goethe's play, and although this edition is now acclaimed as 'one of the supreme illustrated books of the world' (and a first link in the 20th-century tradition of *livres de artistes* in France), it was a long time before it came to be appreciated as such. When exactly or how Soane acquired his copy is not known, but its presence in his library alongside the 'Fermiers' La Fontaine (see cat.6.3) is a measure of the extraordinary distance that his fascination with contemporary French culture carried him during the course of over fifty years of book collecting.

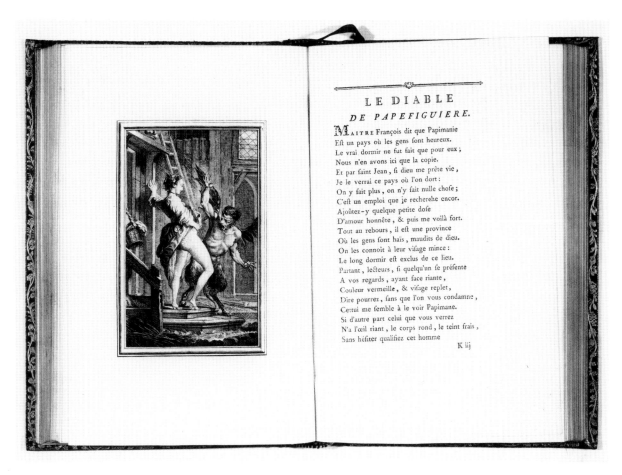

LE DIABLE
DE PAPEFIGUIERE.

MAITRE François dit que Papimanie
Est un pays où les gens sont heureux.
Le vrai dormir ne fut fait que pour eux ;
Nous n'en avons ici que la copie.
Et par saint Jean, si dieu me prête vie,
Je le verrai ce pays où l'on dort :
On y fait plus, on n'y fait nulle chose ;
C'est un emploi que je recherche encor.
Ajoûtez-y quelque petite dose
D'amour honnête, & puis me voilà fort.
Tout au rebours, il est une province
Où les gens sont hais, maudits de dieu.
On les connoit à leur visage mince :
Le long dormir est exclus de ce lieu.
Partant, lecteurs, si quelqu'un se présente
A vos regards, ayant face riante,
Couleur vermeille, & visage replet,
Dire pourrez, sans que l'on vous condamne,
Cettui me semble à le voir Papimane.
Si d'autre part celui que vous verrez
N'a l'œil riant, le corps rond, le teint frais,
Sans hésiter qualifiez cet homme

K iij

FIG.16 'Le Diable de Papefiguière'. Illlustration by Charles Eisen. See cat.6.3.

Religion was not for John Soane. When he designed funeral monuments he steadfastly avoided all Christian symbolism. But his interest in mortality and the depths of a troubled inner spirit was fuelled by works of the romantic imagination, both for the walls of his house and the shelves of his library. Books for Soane were a form of conversation, sometimes with his younger self and sometimes with his own, often angry, psyche. He read and reread the trials and tribulations of his hero *Gil Blas* throughout his long life.

Visual and topographical links to literature were important to him. As a very young man he had sketched Rousseau's tomb at Ermenonville on to the flyleaf of his copy of the *Confessions* and while in Italy was much influenced by his reading of *Julie, ou la Nouvelle Heloise* even if he did not follow his travelling companion John Patteson's example and visit Vevey itself. In later and unhappier times, the sublime extremes of landscape provided catharsis for his moods, as when he visited the craggy gorge outside Harrogate following his wife Eliza's death and empathised with *King Lear*, another parent of ungrateful children.

But it was within the confines of 13 Lincoln's Inn Fields that Soane brought his fascination with the literary Gothic to fulfilment, expressing it architecturally in the subterranean Monk's Parlour in which he, or rather himself as Padre Giovanni, sat moping surrounded by the impedimenta of a religion for which he felt nothing but contempt. Unexplained phenomena, the supernatural of the romantic stage and page, epitomised by the translucent alabaster sarcophagus glowing at the heart of his house and painted by Joseph Gandy, only hinted at the ultimate mystery, Soane's own fate. His reading could do no more than prepare him for uncertainty.

GD

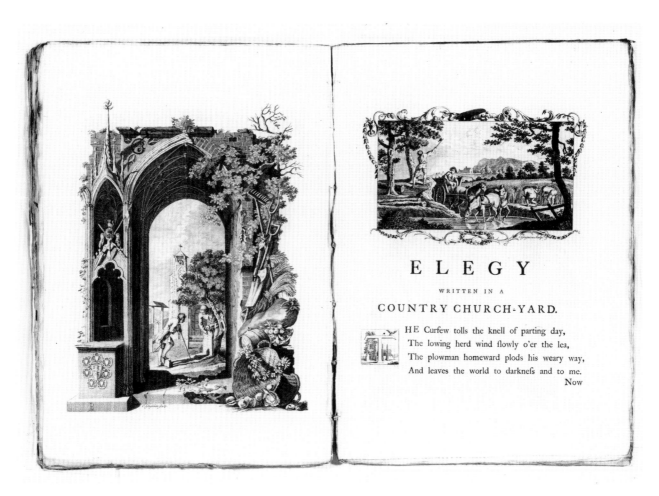

FIG.17 Illustrations by Richard Bentley of Gray's 'Elegy written in a Country Church-yard'. See cat.7.1.

7.1 Thomas Gray (1716–1771)

Designs by Mr. R. Bentley, for six poems by Mr T. Gray, London 1775. 'Elegy in a Country Church-yard'. Etched plate and head-piece, drawn by Richard Bentley (1708–1782) and engraved by Charles Grignion (1715–after 1785). (Fig.17)

Gray's 'Elegy in a Country Church-yard' is one of the most famous and best-loved poems in the English language. Bentley's extraordinarily witty illustrations, which combine classical river gods, rococo lightness and Strawberry Hill gothick, were commissioned by Horace Walpole for the first edition published in 1753. They have been described as 'the most graceful monument to Gothick Rococo' (Kenneth Clark) and 'a turning-point in British decorative art' (Hans Hammelmann). Gray himself wrote that his poems were to be considered as 'subordinate and explanatory to the Drawings' – a notion that seems rather odd today, but which Soane would have appreciated as it assumes a direct association between words, feelings and visual stimuli.

7.2 Jean-Jacques Rousseau (1712–1778)

Les confessions . . . suivies des rêveries du promeneur solitaire, Geneva 1783. Front free end-paper of volume I.

The front free end-paper has a pen and ink sketch by Soane of Rousseau's tomb on the Île des Peupliers in the park at Ermenonville, which was a centre for sentimental pilgrimage, though his body was removed to the Pantheon in Paris in 1794. Rousseau's *Confessions* was a book Soane returned to again and again throughout his life, particularly when his spirit was troubled.

7.3 Robert Blair (1699–1746)

The grave, a poem, London 1808. Plate 32: Death's Door. Etching by Luigi Schiavonetti (1765–1810) after William Blake (1757–1827). (Fig.18)

This poem by Robert Blair was originally written in 1743, but remained continuously in print thereafter. William Blake designed the striking illustrations for this edition. At 'Death's Door' the old man is rushed by a tempest into the darkness of the after-life. Above, renovated man is seated in light and glory. Soane was a subscriber to this volume, along with a number of other members of the Royal Academy.

Drawn by W. Blake.   Etched by L. Schiavonetti.

Death's Door

*'Tis but a Night, a long and moonlefs Night,
We make the Grave our Bed, and then are gone!*

London Published May 1 1808 by Cadell & Davies Strand.

FIG.18 'Death's Door'. See cat.7.3.

7.4 Model of a pedestal

designed by Soane for the cenotaph of William Pitt the Younger in the National Debt Redemption Office, London 1818. Painted plaster SM M522

7.5 Rosary with a cross and miniature carved skull attached.

Wood and mother-of-pearl
SM L125

This rosary was brought back from Italy by the wife of John Flaxman, the sculptor, in 1794. It was later given to Soane by Flaxman's sister-in-law, Maria Denman. The small ivory label attached to it reads : 'Presented to Padre Giovanni' – an allusion to the identification by Soane with the imaginary monk who was supposed to inhabit a room in the basement of 13 Lincoln's Inn Fields.

7.6 William Cheselden

(1688 – 1752)

Osteographia; or the anatomy of the bones, London 1733. Plate XXXVI: The skeleton of a man kneeling on a stone in a posture of prayer. Drawn and engraved by Gerard van der Gucht (1696–1776). (Fig.19)

7.7 'H.B.' [i.e. John Doyle (1797–1868)]

'The funeral of Tory-Principle. Dutifully dedicated to the Holy Alliance'. Hand-coloured aquatint, published *c.* April 1827.

This mock funeral procession, complete with the customary mute, satirises the mass resignation of Tory politicians which followed the appointment of George Canning as Prime Minister in April 1827. Heading the procession of mourners are Lord Eldon (the Lord Chancellor) with a handkerchief to his eye, and the Duke of Wellington.

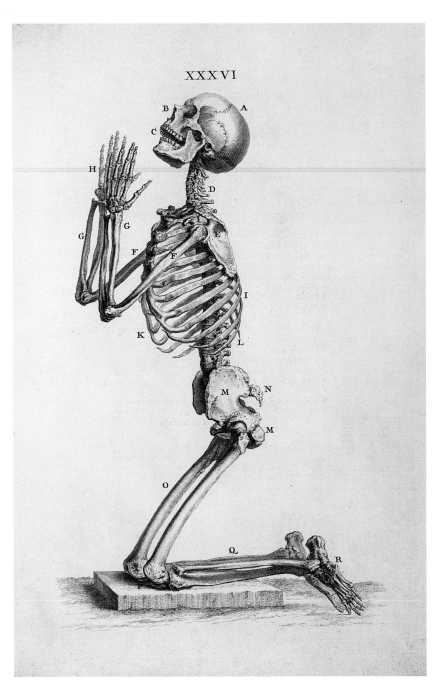

FIG.19 Skeleton of a man praying. See cat.7.6.

Soane was a man of his time in his veneration of Shakespeare as the embodiment of literary genius. Though Shakespeare was read and admired throughout the century-and-a-half after his death, he was also routinely condemned for exhibiting artistic faults: in particular, intermingling tragedy and comedy, and employing elaborate plots with several chronological shifts and changes in scene. But shifts in taste during the eighteenth century, instigated by Samuel Johnson and David Garrick, were built upon by Soane's generation to consolidate what now seems so inevitable: Shakespeare's pre-eminence in the canon of English literature.

Soane paid both visual and verbal homage to Shakespeare, constructing a 'Shakespeare Recess' in his house in Lincoln's Inn Fields, copying extracts from Shakespeare into commonplace books and quoting from him in lectures. He and his family were enthusiastic theatre-goers, witnessing performances of Shakespearian roles from actors whose names are still legendary: Sarah Siddons, John Philip Kemble and Edmund Kean. By their use of expression, gesture and tableau, actors were an important means of modelling Shakespeare's impact on the visual arts, and were sometimes even painted in character – Soane owned a portrait of Kemble as Coriolanus.

The demand for authentic Shakespearean texts had diverse effects in Soane's lifetime. The Shakespeare forgeries of William Henry Ireland – crude as they now seem – testify to the huge contemporary appetite for Shakespeariana, while the quest for authoritative readings undertaken by Shakespeare's editor Edmond Malone revolutionised textual criticism. Soane's holdings were desirable by the standards of any self-respecting contemporary book collector; but they also shed light on his attempts to encourage a British school of painting and explore the British aesthetic, since claims made for Shakespeare were inextricably bound up with those for Britain's artistic contribution to civilisation. AS

8.1 Giambattista Cinzio Giraldi (1504–1573)

De gli hecatommithi di M. Giovanbattista Gyraldi Cinthio, Monte Regale, 1565. Letterpress title-page with printer's woodcut device.

Giraldi's 112 tales compiled in imitation of Boccacio's *Decameron* furnished Shakespeare with plots or themes for *Othello* and *Measure for Measure*.

8.2 William Shakespeare (1564–1616)

Mr. William Shakespeares Comedies, histories & tragedies. Published according to the true originall copies, London 1623. Title-page with portrait of the author engraved by Martin Droeshout (1601–after 1650). (Fig.2)

The Shakespeare First Folio, published in November 1623, seven years after his death, was the first collected edition of Shakespeare's work, and also the first folio-sized book ever published in England devoted exclusively to plays. The portrait of Shakespeare on the title page has become an iconic image over the intervening three hundred and eighty years. The distinguished provenance of this copy would have had an added resonance for Soane: he acquired it at the sale of James Boswell the younger in May 1825, paying £105. Boswell in turn had

bought it at the sale of John Philip Kemble, the actor, in January 1821. It was Boswell who had the volume rebound in its present fine binding of olive green morocco.

EXHIBITED: The 'Second Folio' (1632). Although not of such legendary rarity as the 'First Folio', this edition is highly prized because it contains 'An Epitaph on the admirable Dramaticke Poet, W. SHAKESPEARE' – the first published English poem by the young John Milton (1608–1674).

8.3 John Britton (1771–1857)

Letter dated 4 June 1825

In this letter John Britton describes in a vivid extended hunting metaphor his purchase of the Shakespeare First Folio on Soane's behalf at the Boswell sale:

My dear Sir, / by extraordinary good luck I just / arrived at the death. The game was started when I / entered the field, – though hot in the pursuit, I was / cool and collected at each leap, and not only was the/first when caught, but immediately bag'd the / prize. It is now sent for your larder, where it will / long keep, be always in good flavour, and do honor / to the possessor. It will afford a perpetual standing / dish, on the table of genius & Talent – never create /surfeit, but "increase of appetite" [by] its almost / miraculous

qualities. Hoping to live long, with you, / to participate in "the feast of reason & the flow of soul", which / such a banquet is calculated to afford, is the sincere/ & not unreasonable wish of / Your confirmed friend/ John Britton

Britton was rather prone to purple passages.

8.4 William Shakespeare (1564–1616)

The historie of Henry the Fourth:. . . Newly corrected by William Shake-speare, London 1632. Letterpress title-page.

As well as the 'First Folio', Soane owned the second (1632) third (1664) and fourth (1685) folio editions of Shakespeare's collected plays. This copy of the second quarto edition of *Henry IV, Part I*, which was first published in 1598, was acquired in a group of quarto plays by other authors printed in the 1630s.

8.5 William Shakespeare (1564–1616)

Twenty of the plays of Shakespeare, in four volumes. . . edited by George Steevens, London 1766. David Garrick's copy. (Fig.20)

These two volumes – vol. I with the book plates of Garrick and Soane and vol. IV displaying the contemporary gilt-tooled red morocco binding – are from the fine set that

the editor of this edition, George Steevens, presented to the famous Shakespearean actor David Garrick. Steevens had consulted the quarto editions of Shakespeare's plays in Garrick's library in order to establish more accurate versions of Shakespeare's original text.

8.6 John Britton (1771–1857)

Remarks on the monumental bust of Shakespeare, at Stratford-upon-Avon, London 1816.
Printed wrapper.

Soane owned a cast of the bust of Shakespeare, produced in 1814 by George Bullock for the poet's monument at Stratford-upon-Avon. He made it the focal point of his shrine to the Bard – the so-called 'Shakespeare Recess' in 13 Lincoln's Inn Fields.

8.7 John Hamilton Mortimer (1740–1779)

'Falstaff, Henry IV part 2, Act 5 Sc.4.'
Etching, published 1776. SM P290

Mortimer issued twelve etchings of Shakespearean characters after his own original drawings, in two sets of six in 1775 and 1776. Soane owned copies of all twelve, having acquired them from one of his wife's relatives, Miss Levick, whose uncle had received them direct from Mortimer.

8.8 Office of Sir John Soane

'Façade of Boydell's Shakespeare Gallery, 52 Pall Mall'
Watercolour, dated 10 April 1810
SM 18/7/14

John Boydell (1719–1804), a successful print publisher, set up the Shakespeare Gallery in Pall Mall in 1789 for the exhibition and sale of paintings and engravings by British artists of subjects from the plays of Shakespeare. The Gallery, designed by George Dance the Younger, under whom Soane had trained as an architect, had a façade that featured a portrait relief of Shakespeare with the dramatic Muse on one side and the Genius of Painting on the other. By the time this view of it was produced in 1810 to illustrate one of Soane's lectures as Professor of Architecture at the Royal Academy, the Shakespeare Gallery had gone out of business and its building had turned into the premises of the British Institution.

8.9 Richard Westall (1765–1836)

'Lady Macbeth prevented from stabbing the King by his resemblance to her father as he sleeps'. Watercolour. SM P28

Westall painted five pictures for Boydell's Shakespeare Gallery, and produced eighteen illustrations for the 1802 Boydell edition of Shakespeare's works. This watercolour was not among those engraved for the latter work.

FIG. 20 The gilt-tooled red morocco binding of David Garrick's copy of George Steevens's edition of *Twenty of the Plays of Shakespeare*, London 1766. See cat.8.5.

Napoleon Bonaparte dominated the lives of a generation of Britons. 315,000 soldiers and sailors died in battles with the French between the Revolution of 1789 and Waterloo in 1815. In nursery rhymes children who would not sleep were told that 'Boney' would be at the window: 'Limb from limb he'll tear you, just as pussy tears a mouse'.

Although Napoleon was a bloodthirsty tyrant in the eyes of the great majority of British citizens a significant minority felt alienated by the Tory government which continued the war: political radicals, religious nonconformists and men such as Lord Byron who were 'outsiders' by nature. Many of these men found more to admire in Napoleon than in George IV or the hereditary Bourbon and Hapsburg monarchs.

Soane was a patriot but was also fascinated by the personality, image and genius of England's enemy. He was one of hundreds of thousands of Londoners to visit exhibitions of trophies seized after Waterloo, whether Napoleon's coach, portraits, cutlery or pistols. He bought portraits and relics such as a pistol and a lock of hair and visited Paris in 1814 and 1819. As an architect, he admired Napoleon's reconstruction of Paris in a monumental neo-classical style, which he argued – unsuccessfully – should be the model for a new imperial London.

When Napoleon died in 1821 it suddenly became safe to admire openly the genius of a man who had been the greatest soldier since Alexander the Great and had restored civil order after the chaos of the Revolution. As a self-made man, Soane was impressed by Napoleon's rise from obscurity to being the ruler of half of Europe by the age of 35; and as a Romantic, he was attracted also by the idea of flawed genius and the drama of the rise and fall of a great historical figure.   CW

9.1 Charles Percier (1764–1838) and P. F. L. Fontaine (1762–1853)

Palais, maisons et autres edifices modernes, Paris 1798. Plate 86 (divisional title for cahier XV): A gallery designed in the style of the Vatican *loggie.* Hand-coloured etching. (Fig.21)

Percier and Fontaine presented this splendid hand-coloured copy of their book to Josephine Bonaparte in 1798, before she became Empress. In ordinary copies the plates are uncoloured etchings in the outline manner. In this presentation copy however (one other example of which is known to have existed), these are accompanied by duplicate impressions of all the plates carefully hand-coloured, either by the authors themselves or, more probably, by someone working from their original finished drawings. Soane purchased this copy on a trip to Paris in 1814, the year of Josephine's death. Like many others at the time, he was sentimentally attracted by mementoes of the woman whom Napoleon had divorced to marry the daughter of the Emperor of Austria. As an architect however, he would have also prized this spectacular 'souvenir' as much for its contents – a revolutionary new focus on the architecture and ornament of Renaissance and Baroque houses in Rome – as for the appropriateness of its historical associations.

9.2 John James Masquerier (1778–1855)

A description of the great historical picture . . . of Buonaparte, at the grand review of the consular guard, London 1801. Title-page and etched frontispiece.

This pamphlet was sold as a guide to a huge canvas by Masquerier measuring 27 by 17 feet exhibited in a showroom in Piccadilly in 1801. The picture claimed to show Napoleon's 'short Figure, sallow Pensive Countenance' and awkward way of riding as he reviewed his troops in the courtyard of the Tuileries on 26 December 1800. This was a day on which Napoleon showed Paris that he had not been scared by an assassination attempt two days before; the damage caused by the bomb is visible on the walls behind. By this date there was a multiplicity of prints of Napoleon on sale in London. However Masquerier claimed to have had access to Napoleon at breakfast and boasted that 'This is the ONLY LIKENESS, in London, painted from LIFE'.

9.3 Domenico Marchelli (1764–1832)

Monumento della divozione . . . di Reggio a S.M. l'Imperatore e Re Napoleone, Reggio 1809. Binding bearing the crest and crown of Napoleon and the arms and insignia of the King of Italy. (Back cover)

This work, a testament of the great support for Napoleon in Reggio, near Emilia in Italy, is notable for its handsome binding. The corners of the upper cover are enriched with the crest and crown of Napoleon and in the centre are the coat of arms and insignia of the King of Italy, made up of dyed and painted colour on-lays of morocco and vellum tooled in gilt. The lower cover bears the escutcheon of the town of Reggio.

9.4 Charles Percier (1764–1838) and P. F. L. Fontaine (1762–1853)

Description des cérémonies et fêtes . . . pour le marriage de S.M. l'Empereur Napoléon, Paris 1810. Plate 13: 'L'Empereur et l'Impératrice recevant sur leur Trône les Hommages et les Félicitations de tous les Corps de L'Etat, le lendemain de leur Mariage.* Hand-coloured etching. (Fig.22)

This volume was another of those purchased by Soane on his visit to Paris in 1814 (see cat.9.1). It is in a handsome Empire style binding by Tessier of Paris of gold-tooled red morocco with blue watered-silk end-papers. The hand-coloured plates depict the ceremonies and festivities for the marriage of Napoleon to Princess Marie-Louise of Austria in 1810.

9.5 James Elmes (1782–1862)

Description of the new village of Waterloo, London 1816. Printed paper wrapper.

This proposal by the architect James Elmes for a 'new village of Waterloo' in London's Primrose Hill was an ingenious attempt to

FIG. 21 A gallery designed in the style of the Vatican *loggie*. See cat.9.1.

combine the patriotic euphoria of the moment with the picturesque fashion for houses designed in a variety of foreign styles. The proposed village, which unsurprisingly was never built, was to be divided into quarters, each named after countries in which Napoleon had been defeated, from Egypt, to Russia, Spain and Portugal, and with houses built in the styles of the respective countries. The centrepiece was to be a residential castle named after Mont St-Jean, the village closest to the battlefield of Waterloo.

9.6 Clennell Committee

Proposals for publishing . . . a print representing . . . the decisive charge of the Life Guards at Waterloo . . . from a picture by Luke Clennell, London 1819. Printed prospectus.

The publication of this print was undertaken by a committee formed to assist Clennell's three young children following the double tragedy of their father's mental breakdown in 1817 and their mother's death in the following year. John Britton, the antiquary, was secretary to the committee, and he has added a manuscript note to Soane on the other side, soliciting his support.

9.7 Egyptian Hall, Piccadilly (1816)

Description of a Series of Pictures painted by order of the late Emperor of France . . . now exhibiting at the London Museum, Piccadilly, London 1816. Title-page and etched frontispiece.

After Waterloo there was a huge public demand for exhibitions of trophies seized from Napoleon. Ten thousand people a day had flocked to see Mr Bullock's exhibition of the carriage captured at Waterloo early in 1816. Later the same year Bullock, the proprietor of the London Museum (also known as the Egyptian Hall), put on a second exhibition of trophies he had bought from Napoleon's palaces, including a series of portraits: Napoleon's face was as recognisable to the British as that of Nelson and Wellington. He also displayed personal objects such as pistols and cutlery, and to set the scene he decorated his gallery with the heraldic decorations installed in Notre-Dame for Napoleon's coronation as Emperor in 1804 and subsequently removed by the Bourbons.

9.8 Egyptian Hall, Piccadilly (1821)

Explanatory description of the Battle of Waterloo . . . exhibiting at the Egyptian Hall, Piccadilly, London 1821. Title-page and etched frontispiece.

Of the many artists who painted the battle, James Ward was the only one to present it in allegorical form. Better known today as a painter of animals, his explanation of the picture in this pamphlet consists of moralising reflections on themes of war and peace. Ward's vast canvas, measuring 35 × 24 feet, was presented by the British Institution to the Royal Hospital at Chelsea, where Soane, in his official capacity as Clerk of Works to the Hospital, was faced with the headache of how to display it.

9.9 Buonaparte Reward of £1,000 (1814). Printed broad-sheet.

In April 1814 Napoleon abdicated and was exiled to Elba. The following March, he returned to France and, having broken the terms of his treaty, was declared an outlaw by the Allied Powers. This poster offers a reward of £1,000 to anyone who would capture Napoleon and bring him to Britain to be tried for the murder of British subjects. The authors describe him as 'Signior N. Buonaparte', emphasizing his Italian origins and denying him his imperial title. Napoleon is portrayed as a common criminal since his prosecution under Common Law would demonstrate the virtues of English 'Law and Liberty'.

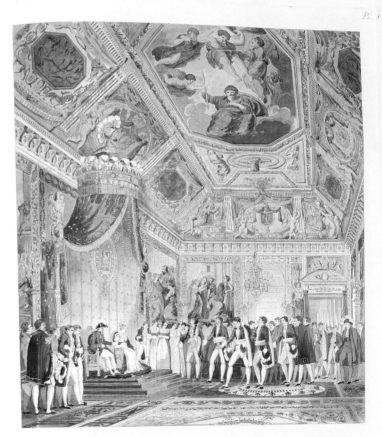

FIG.22 The Emperor and Empress on the morning after their wedding. See cat.9.4.

9.10 a–e Five Napoleonic medals.

Bronze SM SDR 21.7, 36, 68, 96 & 116

Soane had a collection of 140 of these medals, struck at the Paris mint between 1796 and 1815 to celebrate victories and other episodes in Napoleon's career. Produced from 1802 under the direction of Dominique Vivant-Denon, they were designed by a variety of French artists. This particular collection was thought by Soane to have been assembled by Denon for the Empress Josephine.

(a) Inscribed on reverse: Conquete de la Haute Egypte An VII Galle F[ecit]
(b) Inscribed on reverse: Le Traité d'Amiens Rompu par l'Angleterre en Mai de l'An 1803 Jeuffroy Fecit
(c) May 1803. Inscribed on reverse: Napoleon Emp. et Roi. Depaulis F[ecit]
(d) The Imperial Eagle. Inscribed on obverse: 1807 Jaley F[eci]t
(e) Crossing the Danube 5 July 1809. Inscribed on obverse: Traiectus V Iulii MD CCC IX Brenet F[ecit]

— 10 — 'MASTER NASH, MASTER NASH ...'

The two Johns – Nash and Soane – were the most famous London-based architects of their generation. Opposite in appearance, temperament and attitude, their careers followed mutually repellent trajectories. Nash was George IV's favourite architect and stood for everything that Soane hated about the current state of architecture in Britain. Soane was not alone in this poor opinion as the graphic and verbal squibs of 'Peter Pindar', 'Q in the Corner' and 'I. Hume' testify. He loved architecture with a pure and passionate heart, honoured her heroes and studied her beauties in every waking hour. Nash on the other hand dressed her like a whore for cheap flashy effect in order to induce a feeble-minded monarch to waste vast amounts of taxpayer's money on monstrous palaces full of Chinese baubles and Hindoo frippery. But to the chagrin of Soane it was Nash who succeeded in transforming the face of London in the 1820s with brilliant schemes of urban expansion and picturesque street development, in spite of the fact that he, Soane, had been exhibiting his own ideas for such improvements for years on the walls of the Royal Academy. If Soane was at his weakest when faced with criticism, Nash was never more impressive than in a dogfight with his many opponents. The inevitable moment of nemesis for Nash arrived with the death of George IV in 1830. Tied as they were to opposing spokes of fortune's wheel, Nash's nadir was naturally Soane's zenith, for within months of dismissing the architect of Buckingham Palace, the new king had bestowed on Soane the knighthood that the old king had wanted but failed to give to his rival.

NS

10.1 John Taylor (1757–1832), letter dated 16 March 1817

> Master Nash, Master Nash,
> You merit the lash,
> For debauching the taste of your heir
> to the throne:
> Then cross not the Seas,
> To rob the Chinese,
> But learn to be wise from Vitruvius
> and Soane.

John Taylor, the editor and proprietor of the violently Tory 'Sun' newspaper, was one of Soane's oldest and firmest friends. This letter records for his friend's amusement some lines composed by John Wolcot (1738–1819), a celebrated satirist of the day better known by his pen-name 'Peter Pindar'. Wolcot is said to have been plagued by Taylor's incessant puns – a characteristic Regency disease – and maybe came up with this witty doggerel by way of retaliation.

10.2 Engelbert Kaempfer (1651–1716)

The history of Japan . . . written in High-Dutch by Engelbertus Kaempfer. . . and translated from his original manuscript . . . by J. G. Scheuchzer, 2 volumes, London 1727. Vol. I, pl.22: 'Chimaera Japonum & Sinarum' [Fabulous beasts of Japan and China]. Engraving.

The mythical 'Foo Hum' – or royal bird of China (see fig. 7 & 8) – makes numerous appearances in the extraordinary interiors of Nash's Brighton Pavilion. Permitted only to ornament the palace of the Emperor, it was perfectly suited to the task of being simultaneously exotic and flattering – deadly temptations to which Soane was perhaps too knowledgeable and serious about architecture to succumb.

10.3 Lord Berwick's Album of Indian and Persian Miniatures

Fol.1b: A lady seated in a low chair playing a *tambura* – provincial Mughal, first half of 18th century; fol.2a: A girl seated on the stump of a tree playing a *tambura* – provincial Mughal, mid-18th century. Watercolour and gouache.

Soane bought this album of Indian and Persian miniatures for 5 guineas at the sale of the library of Lord Berwick in 1827. Probably of Deccani origin it was assembled around the middle of the 18th century, and first passed into European hands sometime after 7 September 1762. Soane's appreciation of indigenous Indian art shares more with the enlightenment concerns of the Asiatic Society of Bengal (founded 1784) – to dispel ignorance of the history and culture of the sub-continent through scientific study and sympathetic depiction – than with fashionable enthusiasm for the picturesque exoticism of Sezincote (1805) or Nash's Brighton Pavilion (1815–18).

10.4 John Nash (1752–1835)

The Royal Pavilion at Brighton. [London, 1826]. Pl.28: 'Section through the State Apartments'. Hand-coloured and colour-printed aquatint, engraved by John Cleghorn from a drawing by A. C. Pugin. (Fig.23)

This lavish picture-book was commissioned by the Prince Regent shortly before his accession to the throne as George IV in 1820, with the intention that copies might be distributed as marks of royal favour. Although George IV soon lost interest in his bizarre 'palace of varieties' on the south coast, Nash was allowed virtually limitless funds to produce a book that would portray the full splendour of the Pavilion as completed by the King's favourite architect. Soane bought this copy on 7 May 1831 from the booksellers T. & W. Boone for the knock-down price of 5 guineas and 6 pence – almost exactly a quarter of what he would have paid when the book first went on sale to the public in July 1826.

10.5 'Q in the Corner' [i.e. George Cruikshank] (1792–1878)

'Nashional Taste!!! / Dedicated without permission, to the Church Commissioners / Providence sends meat, / The Devil sends Cooks / Parliament sends Funds / But, who sends the Architects?!!!'. Hand-coloured etching published 7 April 1824.

This caricature of Nash impaled upon the spire of All Saints, Langham Place (built 1822–25) appeared a week after he was 'named and shamed' in Parliament over the oddity of its design. Although 'Q in the Corner' was a *nom-de-plume* used by the great caricaturist and illustrator George Cruikshank, the pencilled attribution to the architect Ambrose Poynter (1796–1886) may not been entirely mistaken. Poynter was an excellent draughtsman and, as a former pupil of Nash's, could well have supplied Cruikshank with the likeness that he needed to draw this caricature.

10.6 'I. Hume' [pseudonym]

The palace that N—h built: a parody on an old English poem. [London 1829]. Pl.[2]: 'This is the beautiful Ball in the Cup, / Which the tasteful Committee in wisdom set up / on the top of the Palace that N—H built.' Etching, possibly by G. Davies. (Fig.24)

On the left a naked George IV and Mrs Fitzherbert admire Nash's new dome on the garden front of Buckingham House, while the architect smacks his lips over a long bill. Nash's ill-fated conversion of Buckingham House into a palace for George IV was heavily criticised for being in bad taste and unnecessarily expensive. He was especially vulnerable to charges of incompetence (he ordered the demolition of the new wings he had just completed because they were a hopeless jumble) and venality through artificially increased architect's fees and the awarding of contracts for the supply of materials in which he stood to gain financially. It was precisely Soane's longstanding recognition of the need to avoid such conflicts of interest that was to provide the necessarily sound professional basis for establishing the (Royal) Institute of British Architects in 1834.

FIG.23 'Section through the State Apartments' of the Royal Pavilion at Brighton (detail). See cat.10.4.

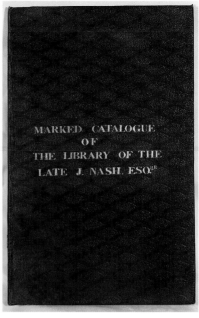

10.7 John Nash (1752–1835)

Catalogue of the valuable architectural and miscellaneous library of the late John Nash . . . sold by auction. London 1835. Copy marked up with buyers' names and hammer prices. Letterpress. (Fig.25)

On his death Nash was rumoured to have left a mountain of debt, forcing his executors to sell his collections and library at East Cowes to pay off creditors. By contrast, less than two years earlier Soane had secured an Act of Parliament 'for the setting up and preserving' of his 'Museum'. Always alert to opportunities of acquiring 'memorials' of deceased British architects that he admired, Soane came away from this sale with only four drawings of Nash's designs. Of greater interest to him was a superb copy of Macklin's Bible (lot 165, hammer price 15 guineas), a significant group of rare architectural books not yet represented in his own library and, above all, an important cache of autograph landscape drawings and ceiling designs by Robert Adam which, unlike the relics of Nash's practice, had already an honoured place in his huge collection of this and other British architects' drawings.

CHRONOLOGY
THE LIFE AND LIBRARY OF SIR JOHN SOANE

A remarkable number of Soane's book acquisitions are recorded in his bills of purchase, diaries, and correspondence, annotated sale catalogues and dated inscriptions in the volumes themselves. There are, however, a great many books for which records of acquisition do not survive, or have not yet been discovered. They may come to light in the completion of the library catalogue.

The following chronology is by no means comprehensive. It is focused on architectural books, which were the tools of Soane's trade as a practising architect and Professor of Architecture at the Royal Academy; even in that field the entries are selective.

LIFE AND EVENTS	BOOK ACQUISITIONS
1753 Birth of John Soan, the youngest child of John Soan, a bricklayer.	
1762	A. Gilby, *The testament of the twelve patriarchs* (1706). Insc. 'John Soan His Book Jul 23 1762 and John Soan is a Nody for Scibbling His Book & ought to have his licking Bought.'
1765 Soane working as a hod boy in the bricklaying trade.	J. Robertson, *Compleat treatise of mensuration* (1739). Handed down by his elder brother, William, who was also in the building trade.
1768 Enters the office of George Dance, the younger. Royal Academy founded.	
1769 Shakespeare Jubilee held at Stratford, Warwickshire. Napolean Bonaparte born.	M. Brettingham, *Holkham* (1761). Presented by the author before his death in August 1769.
1771 Enters the RA Schools.	R. Fréart, *Parallel of the antient architecture with the modern* (1707).
1772 In the office of Henry Holland; wins RA silver medal; exhibits for the first time at the RA.	
1773	J. Gibbs, *Bibliotheca Radcliviana* (1747).
1776 Wins the RA gold medal.	
1777 His prize-winning design presented by Sir William Chambers to George III; RA recommends that he be appointed travelling student to Italy.	J. Baretti, *Manners and customs of Italy* (1768). Lady Anna Miller, *Letters from Italy*, 2 vols (1777).
1778 Publication of Soane's *Designs in architecture*. Travels to Italy, arriving at Rome in May where he met Lord Lord Frederick Hervey, Bishop of Derry, who presented him with Consul Smith's facsmile of the first edition of 1570 of Andrea Palladio's *Quattro libri d'architettura* and B. Galiani's translations of Vitruvius, *L'architettura* (1758).	Clement XIV, *Interesting letters of Pope Clement XIV* (1778). L. Sterne, *Sentimental journey through France and Italy* (1775). T. Whateley, *Observations on modern gardening* (1770).
1779 Visited Bologna, Florence, Sicily, Malta, Milan, Naples, Padua, Parma, Venice, Verona, and Vicenza. An extraordinary eruption of Mount Vesuvius.	S. Maffei, *Verona illustrata* (1779). Roger Shanhagan (i.e. R. Smirke, W. Porden and R. Watson), *The exhibition* (1779), sent to Soane in Rome by his RA friends.
1780 Elected to the Florentine Accademia del Disegno; purchased and copied measured drawings of Michele Sanmichele buildings in Verona; returned to England.	M.-J. Peyre, *Oeuvres d'architecture* (1765). W. Borlase, *The natural history of Cornwall* (1758). W. Borlase, *Antiquities … Of Cornwall*, 2nd ed. (1769).
1781 Commenced London practice; began to concentrate on buying architectural books.	W. Chambers, *Treatise on civil architecture* (1759).
1783	Claude Perrault, *Les dix livres d'architecture de Vitruve* (1673).
1784 Married Elizabeth Smith, niece and heir of George Wyatt, a wealthy builder; began to spell his name with an 'e'.	C.-A. Helvétius, *De l'esprit* (1758).
1785	T. Major, *Ruins of Pæstum* (1768).
1786 John Soane, junior born.	A. Desgodets, *Les edifices antiques de Rome* (1682). J. B. Fischer von Erlach, *Civil and historical architecture* (1737). J. Gwynn, *London and Westminster improved* (1766). T. Malton, *Treatise on perspective* (1779) J. Paine, *Plans, elevations and sections*, vol. I (1767).
1787 Second son, George, born (dies 1788).	W. Coxe, *Travels into Poland, Russia, Sweden and Denmark* (1787), from the author. G. Richardson, *Treatise on the five orders* (1787).
1788 Appointed architect to the Bank of England. Publication of Soane's *Plans … of buildings executed in the counties of Norfolk, Suffolk …* (1788).	A.-C. d'Aviler, *Cours d'architecture.* (1760).
1789 Third son, George, born.	
1790 Death of George Wyatt leaving property, including books, to Elizabeth Soane; establishes an office at Albion Place, Blackfriars; appointed Clerk of Works to St James's Palace, the Houses of Parliament and other public buildings in Westminster; elected to the Society for the Encouragement of Arts, Manufactures and Commerce (now the Royal Society of Arts). First recorded purchase of works of art.	W. Blackstone, *Commentaries on the laws of England*, 8th ed. (1778).

Year	Event	Books
1791	Moves office to Great Scotland Yard, Whitehall. Fourth son Henry, born 1790, dies.	C. Fontana, *Il tempio Vaticano* (1694).
1792	Purchased 12 Lincoln's Inn Fields and began demolition and rebuilding.	W. Chambers, *Treatise*, 3rd ed. (1791), presented by the author. T. Malton, *Tour through the Cities of Westminster and London*, subscription.
1793	Publication of Soane's *Sketches in architecture*; cataloguing his library.	J. Newton trans, *The architecture of M. Vitruvius* (1791). A. Palladio, *L'antichità di Roma*
1794	Moved family and office to 12 Lincoln's Inn Fields.	U. Price, *Essay on the Picturesque* (1794).
1795	Elected Associate of the Royal Academy and Fellow of the Society of Antiquaries; Deputy Surveyor of His Majesty's Woods and Forests. James Playfair sale.	B. F. de Bélidor, *Architecture hydralique* (1737). J.-F. Blondel, *Architecture Français* (1771–77). N. Le Camus de Mezières, *Guide de ceux qui veulent batir* (1786).
1796	Purchases coloured prints of frescoes found in the grounds of Villa Negroni; makes his first purchase of oil paintings.	R. and J. Adam, *Works in architecture* (1778–79) B. F. de Bélidor, *Science des ingénieurs* (1728). C. Cameron, *Baths of the Romans* (1772). T. Daniell, *Oriental Scenery* (1795). J. C. Murphy, *Plans, elevations, sections and views of the church of Batalha* (1795). G. Richardson, *Series of original designs for country seats* (1795). *Vitruvius Britannicus*, 5 vols (1715–1771).
1798	Becomes a magistrate. Sir J. Reynolds sale.	R. Burn, *The Justice of the Peace and the parish officer* (1797).
1799		W. Hamilton, *Campi Phlegræi* (1776–79). J.-J. Rousseau, *Oeuvres*, 37 vols (1788–93).
1800	Pitzhanger Manor purchased and rebuilt.	M.-A. Laugier, *Observations sur l'architecture* (1765).
1801	Earl of Bessborough's sale at which Soane made his first considerable purchase of antique marbles; Willey Reveley sale.	G. Albertolli, *Alcune decorazioni di nobili sale* (1787), and *Ornamenti. Diversi* (1782). C. Fontana, *L'anfiteatro Flavio* (1725). J.-D. Leroy, *Ruines des plus beaux monumens de la Grèce* (1770). A. Palladio, *Les batimens et les desseins*, ed. O. B. Scamozzi (1786). Pliny the Younger, *Historie of the world* (1634–35). D. V.-Denon, *Voyage dans la basse et la haute-Egypte*, 2 vols (1802). £22.
1802	Elected full Royal Academician. Purchases Hogarth's *Rake's Progress*; antique vases from James Clerk sale; a head of Inigo Jones from Edward Burch, and many other works of art for Pitzhanger.	
1803	Becomes a member of the powerful Council of the RA for one year.	P. F. H. d'Hancarville, *Collection of Etruscan, Greek, and Roman antiquities from the cabinet of the Honble Wm. Hamilton* (1766–77). M. A. Lenoir, *Musée des monumens français*, 1st 2 of 8 vols (1800–21).
1804	William Owen paints a portrait of Soane with two of his books, Galiani's Vitruvius and Desgodets, *Edifices antiques de Rome*.	R. Dalton, *Antiquities and views in Greece and Egypt* (1791), coloured plates. C.-N. Ledoux, *L'architecture considérée sous le rapport de l'art* (1804). £18. A. Palladio, *Quattro libri* (1570).
1805	Sale of the contents of Boydell's Shakespeare Gallery from which Soane purchases two paintings: W. Hamilton's *Richard II* and Durno's *Merry Wives of Windsor*.	W. Cheselden, *Osteographia, or the anatomy of the bones* (1753). F. da Colonna, *Hypnerotomachie* (1561). R. Payne Knight, *An analytical inquiry into the principles of taste* (1805). J.-B. De La Rue, *Traité de la coupe des pierres* (1728). Vitruvius. *I dieci libri dell'architettura*, trans. M. A. Barbaro (1556).
1806	Elected Professor of Architecture at the RA; started writing lectures.	Cicero, *Opera*, 10 vols (1783), gift from Hon. George Fulke Lyttleton. J. Gibbs, *Book of Architecture* (1728). J. Gondoin, *Écoles de chirurgie* (1780). A. C. Quatremère de Quincy, *De l'architecture Egyptienne* (1803). J. J. Winckelmann, *Histoire de l'art chez les anciens* (1793–1803).
1807	Appointed Clerk of the Works to Chelsea Hospital; purchases 13 Lincoln's Inn Fields.	I. Jones, *Stonehenge* (1725). J. G. Lavater, *Essays on physiognomy*, 5 vols (1789–98). £25. J. T. Smith, *Antiquities of Westminster* (1807). G. Visconti, *Il museo Pio-Clementino* (1782–96). £37.16.0.
1808	Soane's son 'George finished the Catalogue of the Books by throw'g the Ink on the floor & breaking the Inkstand to pieces'.	M.-A. Laugier, *Essai sur l'architecture*, 2nd ed. (1755). *Museum Florentinum* (1731–66). R. Wood, *Palmyra* (1753).
1809	First lecture at the RA.	T. Daniell, *Hindoo Excavations* (1804) and *Indian Antiquities* (1800).
1810	Pitzhanger sold and contents moved to Lincoln's Inn Fields.	E. Burke, *The sublime and beautiful* (1796).
1811	Soane is appointed architect of Dulwich Picture Gallery.	*Collection complète des tableaux historiques de la revolution français*, 3 vols (1804). £42. B. Taylor, *New Principles of Linear Perspective*, 4th ed. (1811).
1812	Demolition and rebuilding of 13 Lincoln's Inn Fields.	D. Defoe, *A system of magick, or a history of the black art* (1728). A. Palladio, *Fabbriche antiche* (1730).
1813	Moved into 13 Lincoln's Inn Fields.	S. Serlio, *The first (fift) booke of architecture* (1611).
1814	Visit to Paris; appointed one of the Attached Architects to the Office of Works with J. Nash and R. Smirke.	A. Bosse, *La pratique du trait a preuves de Mr Desargues … pour la coup des pierres en l'architecture* (1643). A. Desgodets, MS 'Traité des Ordres d'Architecture'. 15 gns. M.-A. Laugier, *Essay on architecture* (1755). P. Patte, *Monumens érigé en France* (1767). C. Percier and P.-F.-L. Fontaine, *Palais, maisons, et autres édifices modernes à Rome* (1798), Josephine Bonaparte's copy with coloured and uncoloured plates; *Description des cérémonies et des fêtes … pour le mariage de S. M. l'Empereur* (1810), imperial presentation copy with coloured proof impressions; *Maisons de plaisance de Rome* (1809).

1815	Two anonymous articles reviling Soane's architecture published by his son George; death of Mrs Soane.	*Architecture moderne*, publ. By C. A. Jombert (1764). L.-P. Baltard, *Paris et ses monumens* (1803–5). J. F. Blondel, *Cours d'architecture* (1771–77). J. F. Blondel, *De la distribution des maisons* (1737). F. Borromini, *Opera* (1720) A.-H.-V. Grandjean de Montigny, *Architecture Toscane* (1815). E. Kaempfer, *History of Japan* (1727) Vitruvius, *De architectura*, de Laet (1649). W. Newton, *Commentaires sur Vitruve* (1780).
1816	Mrs Sarah (Sally) Conduitt becomes Soane's housekeeper-companion. On his death she was appointed first Inspectress of the museum.	A. Ducarel, *Anglo-Norman antiquities considered* (1767). E.-A. Petitot, *Ragionamento sopra la prospettiva* (1758).
1817	George Dance gives Soane a book of drawings by Sir Christopher Wren.	W. Aglionby, *Painting illustrated in three dialogues* (1685). W. Dodd, *The beauties of Shakespeare* (1810). S. S. Ouvaroff, *Essay on the mysteries of Eleusis … with observations by J. Christie* (1817).
1818	Sale of Robert Adam's library and effects.	P. S. Bartoli, *Picturæ antiquæ cryptarum* Romanarum (1750). G. B. Falda, *Il nuovo teatro della fabriche … de Roma* (1665, 1699). P. Ferrerio, *Palazzi di Roma* (1655). G. J. de' Rossi, *La Fontane di Roma* (1675–85). J. Stuart, *Antiquities of Athens* (1762).
1819	Visits Paris.	C. Quatremère de Quincy, *Considerations sur les arts du dessin en France* (1791). J. J. Rousseau, *Confessions* (1819).
1821	Elected Fellow of the Royal Society.	Marlborough Gems, *Gemmarum antiquarum . . .* (1780, 1791), 2 vols. £80.17.0.
1822		C. Fontana, *Della transportatione dell' obelisco Vaticano* (1590). R. Payne Knight, *Account of the remains of the worship of Priapus* (1786). J.-G. Legrand, *Collection des chefs d'oeuvre de l'architecture des différens peuples … sous la direction de l.-F. Cassas* (1806). G. L. Taylor and E. Cresy, *The architectural antiquities of Rome …* 2 vols (1821–2). £25.4s.
1823	Purchases 14 Lincoln's Inn Fields. Soane's eldest son John dies. Soane buys Hogarth's *Election* series at Mrs Garrick's sale.	L. B. Alberti, *Architecture* (1739). J. Barry, *Series of etchings* (1808). J. A. du Cerceau, *Livre d'architecture* (1582). G. Chaucer, *Workes …* (1602). I. Jones, *Designs of Inigo Jones* (1727). A. Laborde, *Voyage pittoresque … de l'Espagne* (1806–12). £28. M.-A. Laugier, *Essai sur l'architecture* (1753). R. Morris, *Lectures on architecture* (1759). A. Pozzo, *Perspectiva*, J. Sturt engr. (1707). W. Shakespeare, *Twenty of the plays …* (1766), Steevens ed., Garrick's copy.
1825	Soane holds receptions to celebrate his acquisition of the sarcophagus of Sethi I in 1824.	R. Dalton, *Antiquities and views in Greece and Egypt* (1791), coloured plates and drawings. T. Major, *Ruins of Paestum* (1768) with proofs, etchings, additional engravings and drawings; also 63 drawings for the book J. Moyreau, *Oeuvres de Phpe. Wouvermens* (1737–1838). 55 gns. T. Pennant, *Some account of London* (1805), extra illustrated. 650 gns. W. Shakespeare, *…Comedies, histories & tragedies.* (1623), first folio, Kemble's copy. £105.
1826	Sale of the library, etc. of John Sanders of Reigate.	A. C. P. de Thubieres, Comte de Caylus, *Recueil d'antiquities Egyptiennes, Etrusces, Greques et Romaines* (1752–67). J. F. Racknitz, *Darstellung und geschichte des geschmacks der vorzüglichsten Volker* (1794). Album of Indian and Persian miniatures.
1827	Publication of J. Britton's *Union of architecture, sculpture and painting*, a description of Soane's house. Lord Berwick's sale; drawings by Sir William Chambers and Inigo Jones bought from J. Britton.	*The Koran* (1801). T. Pettigrew, *Bibliotheca Sussexiana* (1827), presented by the author.
1828	Publication of Soane's *Designs for public and private buildings*. Portrait of Soane by Sir Thomas Lawrence and bust by Sir Francis Chantrey.	J. G. Legrand, *Essai sur l'histoire generale de l'architecture, nouvelle éd.* (1809). T. R. Underwood, *A narrative of memorable events in Paris …* (1828).
1829	Earl of Guildford's sale. Creation of the Shakespeare Recess.	Dante, *Comento di Christophoro Landino … sopra la comedia di Dante …* (1481/4?). G. C. Giraldi, *De gli Hecatommithi …* (1565).
1830	Sir Thomas Lawrence sale. Publication of *Description of the residence of John Soane*.	D. Loggan, *Oxonia Illustrata* (1675). D. Loggan, *Cantabrigia Illustrata* (c.1702). Royal Academy exhibition catalogues (Lawrence sale). J. J. Winckelmann, *Monumenti antichi inediti …* (1820).
1831	Knighted by William IV.	S. Serlio, *The first (fift) booke of architecture* (1611). W. Zahn, *Die schönsten ornamente … aus Pompeii, Herkulaneum und Stabiae* (1828–9).
1832	Soane publishes *Plans, elevations and perspective views of Pitzhanger Manor House* and new edition of *Description of the residence of John Soane*.	G. Franchetti, *Storia e descrizione del duomo di Milano* (1821), presented by J. Sams. M. Fairfax Somervile, *Mechanism of the heavens* (1831), presented by the author.
1833	*Act for the setting up and preserving of Sir John Soane's Museum* receives Royal Assent. Publication of *Plans, elevations and perspective views of Pitzhanger Manor*; retires as Architect to the Bank of England. Purchases 54 volumes of drawings by Robert and James Adam.	*Description de la Cathedrale de Strasbourg* (1817). J. I. Hittorff, *Architecture antique de la Sicile* (1827). J. I. Hittorff, *Architecture moderne de la Sicile* (1833). J. I. Hittorff, *Les antiquitiés inédités de l'Attique* (1832).
1835	*Memoirs of the professional life of an architect* privately printed; 150 copies of a revised *Description* privately printed. A gold medal presented to Soane by the Architects of England. John Nash sale.	*The Old Testament, embellished with engravings*, ed. T. Macklin (1800). 15 gns. *Description de l'Egypte*, 20 vols (1809–29).
1837	Death of Soane; George Bailey appointed first Curator of the museum.	

SOME SUGGESTIONS FOR FURTHER READING

Richard D. Altick, *The Shows of London*. Cambridge, Mass. and London: The Belknap Press of Harvard University Press, 1978

Allan Braham, *The Architecture of the French Enlightenment*. London: Thames and Hudson, 1980

James Stevens Curl, *The Art and Architecture of Freemasonry*. London: B.T. Batsford Ltd, 1991

James Stevens Curl, *Egyptomania. The Egyptian Revival: a Recurring Theme in the History of Taste*. Manchester and New York: Manchester University Press, 1994

Gillian Darley, *John Soane : An Accidental Romantic*. New Haven and London: Yale University Press, 1999

Hanns Hammelmann, *Book Illustrators in Eighteenth-century England*. New Haven and London: Yale University Press, 1975

Ian Jenkins and Kim Sloan, *Vases and Volcanoes. Sir William Hamilton and his Collection*. London: British Museum Press, 1996

Loftus Jestin, *The Answer to the Lyre : Richard Bentley's Illustrations for Thomas Gray's Poems*. Philadelphia: University of Pennsylvania Press, 1990

E. Tangye Lean, *The Napoleonists. A Study in Political Disaffection 1760–1960*. London: Oxford University Press, 1970.

Brian Lukacher, 'Joseph Gandy and the mythography of architecture', *Journal of the Society of Architectural Historians*, September 1994, pp.280–99

Marco Pellegri, *Ennemondo Alessandro Petitot*. Parma: Tipografia Gia Cooperativa, 1965

Gordon N. Ray, *The Art of the French Illustrated Book 1700–1914*. New York: Pierpoint Morgan Library, 1986

Samuel Schoenbaum, *Shakespeare's Lives*. Oxford: Oxford University Press, 1991

John Summerson, *The Life and Work of John Nash Architect*. London: George Allen & Unwin, 1980

Anthony Vidler, *Claude-Nicolas Ledoux: Architecture and social reform at the end of the Ancien Régime*. Cambridge, Mass. and London: MIT Press, 1990

Giles Waterfield ed., *Soane and Death*. London: Dulwich Picture Gallery, 1996